WeightWatchers®

Comfort Classics

150
Favorite
Home-Style
Dishes

About Weight Watchers

Weight Watchers International, Inc. is the world's leading provider of weight management services, operating globally through a network of Company-owned and franchise operations. Weight Watchers holds over 48,000 weekly meetings, where members receive group support and education about healthful eating patterns, behavior modification, and physical activity. Weight-loss and weight-management results vary by individual. We recommend that you attend Weight Watchers meetings to benefit from the supportive environment you'll find there and follow the comprehensive Weight Watchers program, which includes a food plan, an activity plan, and a behavioral component. In addition, Weight Watchers offers a wide range of products, publications and programs for those interested in weight loss and weight control. For the Weight Watchers meeting nearest you, call **1-800-651-6000.** For information on bringing Weight Watchers to your workplace, call **1-800-8AT-WORK.** Also, visit us at our Web site, **WeightWatchers.com**, or look for *Weight Watchers Magazine* at your newsstand or in your meeting room.

HORSERADISH HAMBURGERS,
PAGE 153

WEIGHT WATCHERS PUBLISHING GROUP

EDITORIAL DIRECTOR NANCY GAGLIARDI
CREATIVE DIRECTOR ED MELNITSKY
PRODUCTION MANAGER ALAN BIEDERMAN
PHOTO EDITOR DEBORAH HARDT
MANAGING EDITOR SARAH WHARTON
EDITORIAL ASSISTANT KRISTINA LUCARELLI
FOOD EDITOR EILEEN RUNYAN
EDITOR JACKIE MILLS
NUTRITION CONSULTANT U. BEATE KRINKE
PHOTOGRAPHER RITA MAAS
FOOD STYLIST ANNE DISRUDE
PROP STYLIST LYNDA WHITE
COVER PROP STYLIST CATHY COOK
ART DIRECTOR JAMES BLASI
ART DIRECTOR/DESIGNER DANIELA HRITCU

ON THE COVER: Skillet Macaroni and Cheese , page 108

About Our Recipes

We make every effort to ensure that you will have success with our recipes. For best results and for nutritional accuracy, please keep these guidelines in mind:

• Recipes in this book have been developed for members who are following the **Momentum**™ plan. We include *POINTS*® values for every recipe. *POINTS* values are assigned based on calories, fat (grams), and fiber (grams) provided for a serving size of a recipe.

• All recipes feature approximate nutritional information; our recipes are analyzed for Calories (Cal), Total Fat (Fat), Saturated Fat (Sat Fat), Trans Fat (Trans Fat), Cholesterol (Chol), Sodium (Sod), Carbohydrates (Carb), Dietary Fiber (Fib), Protein (Prot), and Calcium (Calc).

• Nutritional information for recipes that include meat, poultry, and fish are based on cooked skinless boneless portions (unless otherwise stated), with the fat trimmed.

• We recommend that you buy lean meat and poultry, then trim it of all visible fat before cooking. When poultry is cooked with the skin on, we suggest removing the skin before eating.

• Before serving, divide foods—including any vegetables, accompaniments, or sauce—into portions of equal size according to the designated number of servings per recipe.

• Any substitutions made to the ingredients will alter the "Per serving" nutritional information and may affect the *POINTS* value.

• All fresh fruits, vegetables, and greens in recipes should be rinsed before using.

• All ◆™ **Filling Extra** suggestions have a *POINTS* value of 0 unless otherwise stated.

• Read about the **Simply Filling technique** in Book 6: Keep on Tracking.

CRISPY OVEN-FRIED CHICKEN
WITH SAGE GRAVY, PAGE 133

Contents

ALL-AMERICAN
BREAKFASTS

Chapter 1

HUEVOS RANCHEROS WITH QUESO FRESCO

PREP 10 MIN • COOK 5 MIN • SERVES 4

1   large tomato, diced
1   tablespoon chopped fresh cilantro
1   teaspoon hot pepper sauce
$1/2$ teaspoon salt

$1/8$ teaspoon black pepper
4   large eggs
4   (6-inch) corn tortillas, warmed
4   tablespoons crumbled queso fresco or feta

1 To make the salsa, stir the tomato, cilantro, pepper sauce, salt, and pepper together in a small bowl.

2 Spray a large nonstick skillet with nonstick spray and set over medium heat. Crack the eggs into the skillet, cover, and cook until the whites are completely set and the yolks begin to thicken but are not hard, 3–4 minutes.

3 Place a tortilla on each of 4 plates. Place 1 egg in the center of each tortilla. Spoon $1/2$ cup of the salsa over each egg, and sprinkle with 1 tablespoon of the cheese.

In the Kitchen
Queso fresco is a firm, crumbly Mexican cheese traditionally used for making chiles rellenos. Its flavor is mild and tangy. Use queso fresco in salads and to top chilis and soups.

PER SERVING (1 heuvo ranchero): 151 Cal, 7 g Fat, 2 g Sat Fat, 0 g Trans Fat, 215 mg Chol, 241 mg Sod, 14 g Carb, 2 g Fib, 9 g Prot, 74 mg Calc. **POINTS** value: **3.**

POTATO-AND-GRUYÈRE FRITTATA

4 large eggs	3 small red potatoes, thinly sliced
4 large egg whites	1/2 teaspoon salt
1/2 cup low-fat (1%) milk	1/4 teaspoon black pepper
1/4 cup shredded Gruyère cheese	1 tablespoon unsalted butter
2 tablespoons chopped fresh parsley	4 scallions, thinly sliced

1 Preheat the broiler.

2 Whisk the eggs, egg whites, and milk together in a large bowl until blended. Stir in the cheese and parsley. Set aside.

3 Spray a 10-inch ovenproof nonstick skillet with nonstick spray. Add the potatoes, salt, and pepper and cook, stirring occasionally, until the potatoes begin to soften and brown, 6–8 minutes. Transfer to a plate.

4 Heat the butter in the same skillet. Add the scallions and cook, stirring frequently, until softened, 3 minutes. Return the potatoes to the skillet. Add the egg mixture; reduce the heat to medium-low and cook, undisturbed, until the bottom of the frittata is firm, 8–10 minutes.

5 Place the skillet under the broiler and broil 5 inches from the heat until the frittata is set in the center, 3 minutes. Cut into 4 wedges.

> ▶ **Filling Extra**
> For lunch or a light dinner, pair the frittata with a wedge of melon (1/2 of a medium honeydew melon will increase the **POINTS** value by **1**).

PER SERVING (1/4 of frittata): 257 Cal, 11 g Fat, 5 g Sat Fat, 0 g Trans Fat, 229 mg Chol, 459 mg Sod, 25 g Carb, 3 g Fib, 15 g Prot, 172 mg Calc. **POINTS** value: **5.**

BACON, TOMATO, AND CHEDDAR FRITTATA

PREP 10 MIN • **COOK/BROIL** 20 MIN • **SERVES** 4

1   medium onion, chopped
3   large eggs
3   large egg whites
1   cup fat-free milk
$^1/_8$ teaspoon black pepper

4   slices Canadian bacon, chopped
1   large tomato, chopped
1   cup shredded fat-free cheddar
Chives (optional)

1 Spray a 10-inch ovenproof nonstick skillet with nonstick spray and set over medium heat. Add the onion and cook, stirring occasionally, until softened, 5 minutes. Transfer to a small bowl.

2 Preheat the broiler.

3 Whisk the eggs, egg whites, milk, and pepper in a large bowl until blended. Stir in the onion, bacon, tomato, and cheese.

▶ **Filling Extra**
Chop 1 small red bell pepper and cook it with the onion in step 1. This recipe works with the **Simply Filling technique.**

4 Wipe the skillet clean; spray with nonstick spray and set over medium heat. Add the egg mixture, reduce the heat to medium-low, and cook, undisturbed, until the bottom of the frittata is firm, 8–10 minutes.

5 Place the skillet under the broiler and broil 5 inches from the heat until the frittata is set in the center, 3 minutes. Cut into 4 wedges. Garnish with chives, if using.

PER SERVING ($^1/_4$ of frittata): 198 Cal, 8 g Fat, 3 g Sat Fat, 0 g Trans Fat, 178 mg Chol, 711 mg Sod, 9 g Carb, 1 g Fib, 22 g Prot, 312 mg Calc. *POINTS* value: **4.**

BACON, TOMATO, AND
CHEDDAR FRITTATA

Canadian Bacon, Spinach, and Mushroom Crustless Quiche

PREP 15 MIN • COOK/BAKE 45 MIN • SERVES 6

2   teaspoons olive oil
1   onion, finely chopped
2   slices Canadian bacon, diced
1   (8-ounce) package sliced fresh mushrooms
2   large eggs
2   large egg whites
$^1/_2$ cup fat-free milk

1   cup fat-free ricotta
$^1/_2$ teaspoon dried thyme
$^1/_2$ teaspoon salt
$^1/_4$ teaspoon black pepper
1   (10-ounce) package frozen chopped spinach, thawed and squeezed dry

1 Preheat the oven to 375°F. Spray a 9-inch glass pie plate with nonstick spray.

2 Heat the oil in a large nonstick skillet and set over medium-high heat. Add the onion and cook, stirring occasionally, until softened, 5 minutes. Add the bacon and mushrooms and cook, stirring occasionally, until the mushrooms are softened and most of the liquid has evaporated, 5 minutes.

3 Whisk the eggs, egg whites, milk, ricotta, thyme, salt, and pepper in a large bowl until blended. Stir in the onion mixture and the spinach.

4 Pour into the prepared pie plate. Bake until the top is golden and a knife inserted into the center comes out clean, 35–40 minutes. Let stand 10 minutes before slicing.

◗ Filling Extra
Serve with 6 cups mixed melon balls (1 cup melon balls per serving will increase the **POINTS** value by **1**). This recipe works with the **Simply Filling technique.**

PER SERVING (⅙ of quiche): 125 Cal, 4 g Fat, 1 g Sat Fat, 0 g Trans Fat, 79 mg Chol, 416 mg Sod, 9 g Carb, 2 g Fib, 14 g Prot, 157 mg Calc. **POINTS** value: **2.**

SUNDAY-MORNING GREEK STRATA WITH FETA AND DILL

PREP 20 MIN • **BAKE** 40 MIN • **SERVES** 6

2 (6-inch) whole-wheat pita breads, each cut into 4 wedges

4 large eggs

4 large egg whites

1½ cups low-fat (1%) milk

1 cup low-fat cottage cheese

⅓ cup crumbled feta

1 cup thawed frozen peas

¼ cup chopped fresh dill

1 teaspoon grated lemon zest

¼ teaspoon black pepper

2 medium tomatoes, each cut into 4 slices

1 Preheat the oven to 350°F. Spray a 13 x 9-inch baking dish with nonstick spray.

2 Place the pita wedges on a baking sheet and bake until lightly toasted, 5 minutes. Maintain the oven temperature.

3 Whisk the eggs and egg whites in a large bowl until blended.

4 Put the milk, cottage cheese, and feta in a blender or a food processor and puree until smooth. Add the milk mixture, peas, dill, lemon zest, and pepper to the eggs and stir until blended.

In the Kitchen
To make a day ahead, follow the recipe through step 5, then cover and refrigerate. Add the tomato slices and let stand at room temperature for 15 minutes before baking.

5 Arrange the pita wedges in the baking dish. Pour the egg mixture over the pitas and let stand 10 minutes.

6 Arrange the tomato slices evenly over the strata and bake until lightly browned and the center is set, 35-40 minutes. Cut into 6 pieces.

PER SERVING (⅙ of strata): 216 Cal, 7 g Fat, 3 g Sat Fat, 0 g Trans Fat, 155 mg Chol, 464 mg Sod, 20 g Carb, 3 g Fib, 18 g Prot, 171 mg Calc. *POINTS* value: *4.*

WESTERN OMELETTE
SANDWICHES

Western Omelette Sandwiches

6 large eggs
2 tablespoons chopped fresh parsley
¼ teaspoon salt
⅛ teaspoon black pepper
1 medium onion, finely chopped

1 green bell pepper, diced
4 ounces low-sodium lean deli ham, diced
¼ cup ketchup
4 whole-wheat English muffins, split and toasted

1 Whisk the eggs, parsley, salt, and pepper in a medium bowl until blended.

2 Spray a medium nonstick skillet with nonstick spray and set over medium-high heat. Add the onion, bell pepper, and ham and cook, stirring occasionally, until the vegetables are softened, 5 minutes. Transfer to a bowl.

3 Wipe the skillet clean, spray with nonstick spray, and set over medium-high heat. Add half of the egg mixture. Cook, lifting the edges frequently with a spatula to allow the uncooked egg to run underneath, until the eggs are just set, about 3 minutes. Spoon half of the onion mixture over the eggs. Loosen the edges of the eggs and fold over to enclose the filling. Reduce the heat to low and cook until the eggs are just set, about 1 minute longer.

4 Slide the omelette onto a plate; keep warm. Repeat with the remaining egg mixture and onion mixture to make 1 more omelette.

5 Spread the ketchup evenly on each slice of the English muffins. Place half an omelette on each of 4 of the muffin halves. Top each with a remaining muffin half.

PER SERVING (1 sandwich): 324 Cal, 11 g Fat, 3 g Sat Fat, 0 g Trans Fat, 333 mg Chol, 997 mg Sod, 36 g Carb, 6 g Fib, 22 g Prot, 230 mg Calc. **POINTS** value: **7.**

TEX-MEX BREAKFAST BURRITOS

PREP 10 MIN • **COOK** 5 MIN • **SERVES** 4

4   large eggs

4   large egg whites

$^1/_4$ teaspoon hot pepper sauce

$^1/_8$ teaspoon black pepper

4   (6-inch) whole-wheat tortillas, warmed

1   cup salsa

1   cup shredded fat-free Monterey Jack

4   tablespoons chopped fresh cilantro

1 Whisk the eggs, egg whites, hot sauce, and pepper in a medium bowl until blended.

2 Spray a large nonstick skillet with nonstick spray and set over medium-high heat. Add the egg mixture and cook, stirring often, until just set, about 3 minutes.

3 Spoon one-fourth of the egg mixture onto each tortilla. Top each one with $^1/_4$ cup of the salsa, $^1/_4$ cup of the cheese, and 1 tablespoon of the cilantro. Fold the two opposite sides of each tortilla to enclose the filling.

▶ **Filling Extra**
Stir $^1/_2$ cup finely chopped red bell pepper and 2 thinly sliced scallions into the egg mixture before cooking.

PER SERVING (1 burrito): 216 Cal, 7 g Fat, 2 g Sat Fat, 0 g Trans Fat, 217 mg Chol, 952 mg Sod, 19 g Carb, 3 g Fib, 21 g Prot, 300 mg Calc. **POINTS** value: **4.**

"Pumpkin Pie" Pancakes

PREP 10 MIN • COOK 10 MIN • SERVES 4

1/4 cup all-purpose flour
1/4 cup whole-wheat flour
3 tablespoons packed brown sugar
3/4 teaspoon baking powder
1/4 teaspoon baking soda
1 teaspoon pumpkin pie spice

1/4 teaspoon salt
2/3 cup low-fat buttermilk
1/4 cup canned pumpkin puree
4 teaspoons unsalted butter, melted
1 large egg
4 tablespoons maple syrup

1 Whisk together the all-purpose and whole-wheat flours, brown sugar, baking powder, baking soda, pumpkin pie spice, and salt in a medium bowl. Whisk the buttermilk, pumpkin, butter, and egg in another bowl until blended. Add the flour mixture to the buttermilk mixture, stirring just until blended.

2 Spray a large nonstick skillet or griddle with nonstick spray and set over medium heat. When a drop of water sizzles on it, pour the batter onto the skillet by scant 1/4 cupfuls. Cook just until bubbles begin to appear at the edges of the pancakes, 2–3 minutes. Flip and cook until golden, 2–3 minutes longer. Repeat with the remaining batter, making a total of 8 pancakes. Serve with the maple syrup.

In the Kitchen
Pure maple syrup is the boiled sap from maple trees. It is distinctly more flavorful than artificially-flavored pancake syrups.

PER SERVING (2 pancakes with 1 tablespoon maple syrup): 222 Cal, 6 g Fat, 3 g Sat Fat, 0 g Trans Fat, 65 mg Chol, 383 mg Sod, 39 g Carb, 2 g Fib, 5 g Prot, 138 mg Calc. **POINTS** value: **5.**

GINGER WAFFLES WITH STRAWBERRY-PEACH SAUCE

PREP 20 MIN • COOK 15 MIN • SERVES 8

1   cup strawberries, hulled and sliced or whole thawed frozen strawberries

2   peaches, peeled, pitted, and sliced or 1$^1/_2$ cups thawed frozen peach slices

2   tablespoons orange juice

1   tablespoon honey

1   teaspoon vanilla extract

$^3/_4$ cup all-purpose flour

$^3/_4$ cup whole-wheat flour

3   tablespoons sugar

1$^1/_2$ teaspoons ground ginger

1$^1/_2$ teaspoons baking soda

1$^3/_4$ cups low-fat buttermilk

2   large eggs, separated

2   tablespoons unsalted butter, melted

1 Put the strawberries, peaches, orange juice, honey, and $^1/_2$ teaspoon of the vanilla in a food processor and puree until smooth. Reserve the sauce.

2 Preheat a waffle baker according to the manufacturer's directions.

3 Whisk together the all-purpose and whole-wheat flours, sugar, ginger, and baking soda in a large bowl. Whisk the buttermilk, egg yolks, butter, and the remaining $^1/_2$ teaspoon vanilla in another bowl until blended. Add the buttermilk mixture to the flour mixture, stirring until well blended.

4 With an electric mixer on high speed, beat the egg whites in a medium bowl until soft peaks form, about 2 minutes. Gently fold the beaten whites into the batter until no streaks of white remain.

5 When the waffle baker is ready, pour the batter onto the center and quickly spread to within 1 inch of the edges. Close the baker and bake as the manufacturer directs; do not open until done. Repeat, reheating the waffle baker before adding the next batch of batter. Serve waffles at once with the sauce.

◗ **Filling Extra**
Top each serving of these crispy waffles with $^1/_2$ cup of fresh raspberries or blueberries.

PER SERVING (1 waffle with 3 tablespoons sauce): 198 Cal, 5 g Fat, 3 g Sat Fat, 0 g Trans Fat, 63 mg Chol, 309 mg Sod, 32 g Carb, 3 g Fib, 7 g Prot, 81 mg Calc. **POINTS** value: **4.**

GINGER WAFFLES WITH
STRAWBERRY-PEACH SAUCE

BREAKFAST PORRIDGE WITH BLUEBERRIES

PREP 5 MIN • COOK 15 MIN • SERVES 2

1¹/₂ cups fat-free milk
Pinch salt
¹/₄ cup quick-cooking barley
¹/₄ cup bulgur

¹/₄ cup old-fashioned rolled oats
¹/₂ cup blueberries
2 tablespoons packed brown sugar
Pinch ground cinnamon

1 Put the milk and salt in a small saucepan and bring just to a boil. Stir in the barley, bulgur, and oats. Reduce the heat and simmer, stirring frequently, until the milk is absorbed and the grains are tender, but still chewy, about 10 minutes.

2 Remove from the heat and stir in the blueberries. Spoon the porridge evenly into 2 serving bowls; sprinkle evenly with the remaining brown sugar and cinnamon.

In the Kitchen
The porridge has a hearty, chewy texture. If you prefer it softer and creamier, add ¹/₄ cup water with the milk and simmer a few minutes longer.

PER SERVING (1 bowl): 313 Cal, 1 g Fat, 0 g Sat Fat, 0 g Trans Fat, 4 mg Chol, 159 mg Sod, 66 g Carb, 6 g Fib, 12 g Prot, 255 mg Calc. **POINTS** value: **6.**

Honey-Almond Oatmeal with Strawberries

PREP 5 MIN • COOK 5 MIN • SERVES 4

2 cups fat-free milk

4 teaspoons honey

$^1/_4$ teaspoon cinnamon

$^1/_4$ teaspoon salt

2 cups uncooked instant oatmeal

1 cup sliced strawberries

4 tablespoons sliced almonds, toasted

1 Combine the milk, honey, cinnamon, and salt in a medium saucepan and bring to a boil. Add the oatmeal; reduce the heat and cook, stirring often, until thickened, 1 minute.

2 Divide the oatmeal between 4 bowls. Top evenly with the strawberries and almonds.

PER SERVING (1 cup oatmeal, $^1/_4$ cup sliced strawberries, 1 tablespoon sliced almonds): 251 Cal, 5 g Fat, 1 g Sat Fat, 0 g Trans Fat, 2 mg Chol, 305 mg Sod, 42 g Carb, 5 g Fib, 10 g Prot, 316 mg Calc. *POINTS* value: *5.*

CINNAMON DUTCH BABY WITH
APPLESAUCE AND SOUR CREAM

CINNAMON DUTCH BABY WITH APPLESAUCE AND SOUR CREAM

1   cup all-purpose flour
2   tablespoons sugar
1/4 teaspoon cinnamon
2   large eggs
2   large egg whites

3/4 cup low-fat (1%) milk
1   tablespoon unsalted butter
1   cup unsweetened chunky applesauce
2   teaspoons lemon juice
1/4 cup fat-free sour cream

1 Place a 10-inch ovenproof skillet in the oven. Preheat the oven to 425°F.

2 Whisk together the flour, sugar, and cinnamon in a large bowl. Whisk the eggs, egg whites, and milk in another bowl until blended. Add the egg mixture to the flour mixture, stirring until just combined.

3 Carefully remove the skillet from the oven. Place the butter in the skillet and swirl so that the butter melts and coats the skillet. Pour the batter into the skillet, return it to the oven and bake until the pancake is puffed and browned, about 15 minutes.

In the Kitchen
A Dutch baby is sometimes called a German pancake. You can serve it with any seasonal fresh fruit and a sprinkle of confectioners' sugar instead of the applesauce.

4 Meanwhile, place the applesauce in a microwave-safe bowl and cover with plastic wrap. Prick a few holes in the plastic and microwave on High until heated through, 1 minute.

5 Brush the pancake with the lemon juice. Cut into 4 wedges and place on 4 plates. Top evenly with the applesauce and sour cream.

PER SERVING (1 wedge with 1/4 cup applesauce and 1 tablespoon sour cream): 268 Cal, 6 g Fat, 3 g Sat Fat, 0 g Trans Fat, 117 mg Chol, 103 mg Sod, 42 g Carb, 2 g Fib, 10 g Prot, 96 mg Calc. *POINTS* value: *5.*

PEANUT BUTTER–BANANA SMOOTHIES

PREP 5 MIN • **COOK** NONE • **SERVES** 4

1   medium banana, peeled and cut into
    1-inch chunks
1   cup fat-free milk

1   cup vanilla fat-free yogurt
1   cup ice cubes
1½ tablespoons peanut butter

Put all of the ingredients in a blender; blend on high speed, stopping the blender occasionally to push the fruit and uncrushed ice cubes down with the handle of a wooden spoon, until smooth. Serve at once.

PER SERVING (¾ cup): 132 Cal, 3 g Fat, 1 g Sat Fat, 0 g Trans Fat, 3 mg Chol, 88 mg Sod, 21 g Carb, 2 g Fib, 6 g Prot, 176 mg Calc. **POINTS** value: **2.**

Tropical-Fruit Salsa and Yogurt Parfaits

PREP 15 MIN • **COOK** NONE • **SERVES** 4

1 large mango, peeled, pitted, and cubed	1 tablespoon lime juice
1 cup cubed papaya	1 teaspoon sugar
1 cup cubed pineapple	4 cups plain fat-free yogurt
2 kiwis, peeled and cubed	4 tablespoons unsweetened coconut, toasted
2 tablespoons chopped fresh mint	4 mint sprigs, for garnish (optional)

1 To make the salsa, stir the mango, papaya, pineapple, kiwi, mint, lime juice, and sugar together in a large bowl.

2 Spoon $1/2$ cup of the salsa into each of 4 parfait glasses; top each with $1/2$ cup of the yogurt. Repeat layering once. Sprinkle the parfaits with the coconut and garnish with the mint sprigs (if using).

PER SERVING (1 parfait): 267 Cal, 4 g Fat, 3 g Sat Fat, 0 g Trans Fat, 5 mg Chol, 195 mg Sod, 45 g Carb, 4 g Fib, 16 g Prot, 523 mg Calc. **POINTS** value: **5.**

RASPBERRY-OATMEAL MUFFINS WITH ORANGE GLAZE

PREP 15 MIN • BAKE 20 MIN • SERVES 12

1   cup all-purpose flour
1/2 cup rolled (old-fashioned) oats
1/2 cup wheat germ
1/2 cup packed brown sugar
1   teaspoon baking powder
1/4 teaspoon baking soda
1/4 teaspoon salt

1   cup fat-free vanilla yogurt
1/4 cup butter, melted and cooled
1   large egg
1   tablespoon grated orange zest
1   cup fresh or unthawed frozen raspberries
3   tablespoons confectioners' sugar
1   tablespoon orange juice

1 Preheat the oven to 400°F. Line 12 muffin cups with paper liners; spray the liners with nonstick spray.

2 Whisk together the flour, oats, wheat germ, brown sugar, baking powder, baking soda, and salt in a large bowl. Whisk the yogurt, butter, egg, and orange zest in another bowl until smooth. Add the yogurt mixture to the flour mixture, stirring just until blended. Gently fold in the raspberries.

3 Spoon the batter into the cups, filling each cup about two-thirds full. Bake until a toothpick inserted into a muffin comes out clean, about 20 minutes. Immediately remove the muffins from the pan and cool completely on a rack.

4 To make the glaze, whisk the confectioners' sugar and orange juice in a small bowl until smooth. With a spoon, drizzle the glaze evenly over the top of the cooled muffins. Let stand until the glaze sets, 10 minutes.

PER SERVING (1 muffin): 173 Cal, 5 g Fat, 3 g Sat Fat, 0 g Trans Fat, 28 mg Chol, 162 mg Sod, 28 g Carb, 2 g Fib, 5 g Prot, 74 mg Calc. *POINTS* value: *3.*

ALMOND FRENCH TOAST WITH CRANBERRY-PEAR COMPOTE

PREP 15 MIN • **COOK** 20 MIN • **SERVES** 4

1   cup fresh or thawed frozen cranberries
1   large firm pear, peeled and chopped
1   medium navel orange, peeled and
    coarsely chopped
3/4 cup apple cider
1/4 cup + 1 tablespoon packed brown sugar

2   tablespoons minced peeled fresh ginger
1/2 teaspoon cinnamon
1   cup fat-free egg substitute
1/2 teaspoon almond extract
8   thin slices multigrain bread

1 Combine the cranberries, pear, orange, apple cider, 1/4 cup of the brown sugar, ginger, and cinnamon in a medium saucepan and bring to a boil. Reduce the heat and simmer, covered, until the pears are tender, 12–15 minutes.

2 Whisk the egg substitute, the remaining 1 tablespoon brown sugar, and the almond extract in a large shallow bowl until blended. Add 2 slices of the bread and let stand until evenly soaked, 30 seconds per side. Transfer to a plate. Repeat with the remaining bread.

3 Spray a large nonstick skillet with nonstick spray and set over medium-high heat. Add 2 pieces of the bread and cook until browned, 2–3 minutes on each side. Transfer to a platter and keep warm. Repeat with the remaining bread. Serve with the compote.

PER SERVING (2 slices French toast with 1/3 cup compote): 298 Cal, 2 g Fat, 0 g Sat Fat, 0 g Trans Fat, 0 mg Chol, 341 mg Sod, 60 g Carb, 8 g Fib, 13 g Prot, 192 mg Calc. **POINTS** value: **5.**

RISE-AND-SHINE APRICOT-GINGER SCONES

PREP 15 MIN • **BAKE** 15 MIN • **SERVES** 12

1   cup all-purpose flour

1   cup whole-wheat pastry flour

1½ teaspoons baking powder

½   teaspoon salt

¼   teaspoon ground allspice

4   tablespoons cold butter, cut into small pieces

½   cup diced dried apricots

¼   cup chopped crystallized ginger

½   cup + 2 tablespoons low-fat (1%) milk

½   cup maple syrup

1   large egg

1 Preheat the oven to 400°F. Spray 1 large baking sheet with nonstick spray.

2 Put the all-purpose and whole-wheat flours, baking powder, salt, and allspice in the bowl of a food processor. Add the butter and pulse until the mixture resembles coarse meal. Transfer to a large bowl and stir in the apricots and ginger.

3 Whisk ½ cup of the milk, maple syrup, and egg in a medium bowl until smooth. Add the milk mixture to the flour mixture, stirring until just moistened.

4 Cut the dough into 2 pieces. Roll or pat each piece into a 6-inch circle. Score each circle into 6 triangles. Place on baking sheet. Brush the tops with remaining 2 tablespoons milk. Bake until lightly browned and a toothpick inserted into the middle comes out clean, 15-20 minutes. Transfer to a rack and let cool 5 minutes. Separate into 12 scones. Serve warm or let cool completely.

In the Kitchen
Whole-wheat pastry flour, also called graham flour, is made from finely ground low-protein wheat. If it is unavailable, you can substitute regular whole-wheat flour.

PER SERVING (1 scone): 184 Cal, 5 g Fat, 3 g Sat Fat, 0 g Trans Fat, 28 mg Chol, 204 mg Sod, 33 g Carb, 2 g Fib, 4 g Prot, 76 mg Calc. **POINTS** value: **4.**

RISE-AND-SHINE
APRICOT-GINGER
SCONES

TAKE COMFORT TO LUNCH

Chapter 2

SMOKED TURKEY, CHEESE, AND APPLE WRAPS

PREP 15 MIN • COOK NONE • SERVES 2

2 tablespoons fat-free mayonnaise

1 teaspoon Dijon mustard

1/4 teaspoon curry powder

2 (8-inch) whole-wheat tortillas

2 lettuce leaves

3 ounces (4 slices) thin-sliced smoked deli turkey breast

2 ounces (4 slices) thin-sliced reduced-fat deli Swiss cheese

1/2 small cucumber, thinly sliced

1/2 apple, cored and thinly sliced

1 tablespoon dried cranberries

1 Stir the mayonnaise, mustard, and curry powder together in a small bowl.

2 Place 1 tortilla on a work surface and spread with half of the mayonnaise mixture. Layer the lettuce, turkey, cheese, cucumber, apple, and cranberries down the center. Fold the short sides over the filling, then roll up jelly-roll-style to enclose the filling. Repeat with the remaining ingredients to make 1 more wrap. Cut each wrap in half and serve at once. Or wrap in plastic wrap and refrigerate up to 24 hours.

PER SERVING (1 wrap): 245 Cal, 5 g Fat, 2 g Sat Fat, 0 g Trans Fat, 28 mg Chol, 1,152 mg Sod, 33 g Carb, 6 g Fib, 19 g Prot, 238 mg Calc. *POINTS* value: *5.*

TUNA NIÇOISE SANDWICHES

PREP 15 MIN • COOK NONE • SERVES 2

2 teaspoons Dijon mustard

2 teaspoons red-wine vinegar

1/2 teaspoon olive oil

2 whole-wheat hero rolls, halved horizontally

1 tomato, sliced

1 (6-ounce) can light tuna in water, drained and flaked

4 pitted kalamata olives, thinly sliced

1 hard-cooked egg, peeled and sliced

3 radishes, thinly sliced

2 lettuce leaves

1 Stir the mustard, vinegar, and oil together in a small bowl. Remove and discard some of the soft crumbs from the centers of the rolls. Brush 1/3 of the mustard mixture over the cut sides of the rolls.

2 Layer the tomato slices and the tuna on the bottom halves of the rolls. Drizzle with half of the remaining mustard mixture. Top with the olives and egg. Drizzle with the remaining mustard mixture and top with the radishes and lettuce leaves. Cover with the tops of the rolls and press the sandwiches lightly. Cut each sandwich in half and serve at once. Or wrap in plastic wrap and refrigerate up to 6 hours.

▸ **Filling Extra**
Add roasted red bell peppers (not packed in oil), sliced cucumbers, or thinly sliced red onion to the sandwiches.

PER SERVING (1 sandwich): 258 Cal, 7 g Fat, 2 g Sat Fat, 0 g Trans Fat, 129 mg Chol, 668 mg Sod, 19 g Carb, 4 g Fib, 29 g Prot, 86 mg Calc. *POINTS* value: **5.**

New Orleans Muffaletta Sandwich

PREP 15 MIN • COOK NONE • SERVES 4

1 celery stalk, finely chopped

1/2 cup giardiniera, rinsed, drained, and chopped

1/4 cup pimiento-stuffed green olives, sliced

1 garlic clove, minced

Pinch dried oregano

1 8-ounce whole-wheat French bread loaf or round, halved horizontally

4 ounces (4 slices) reduced-fat deli provolone

6 ounces (8 thin slices) deli turkey ham

1 Stir the celery, giardiniera, olives, garlic, and oregano together in a small bowl.

2 Remove and discard some of the soft crumbs from the center of the bread. Spoon the celery mixture evenly on the bottom of the bread. Top evenly with the cheese and ham. Cover with the top of the bread. Cut the sandwich into fourths and serve at once. Or wrap in plastic wrap and refrigerate up to 6 hours.

In the Kitchen

Giardiniera is a bottled Italian pickled vegetable mixture usually containing carrots, celery, cauliflower, red peppers, hot peppers, and onion.

PER SERVING (1/4 of sandwich): 274 Cal, 11 g Fat, 5 g Sat Fat, 0 g Trans Fat, 43 mg Chol, 1,105 mg Sod, 25 g Carb, 2 g Fib, 21 g Prot, 274 mg Calc. *POINTS* value: **6.**

NEW ORLEANS
MUFFALETTA
SANDWICH

HUMMUS, FETA, AND SALAD PITAS

PREP 15 MIN • **COOK** NONE • **SERVES** 2

$1/2$ small cucumber, peeled, quartered lengthwise, and sliced

3 tablespoons crumbled reduced-fat feta

4 pitted kalamata olives, chopped

2 teaspoons red-wine vinegar

$1/8$ teaspoon salt-free garlic-herb seasoning

2 (6-inch) whole-wheat pitas, halved

4 lettuce leaves

1 tomato, thinly sliced

$1/2$ cup prepared hummus

1 Stir the cucumber, feta, olives, vinegar, and garlic-herb seasoning together in a small bowl.

2 Stuff each pita half evenly with the lettuce, tomato, hummus, and the cucumber mixture. Serve at once. Or, if packing the sandwiches for lunch, store servings of the cucumber mixture in separate containers and add to the sandwiches just before eating. Or wrap the sandwiches in plastic wrap and refrigerate up to 6 hours.

◗ Filling Extra
Serve the sandwiches with strips of red and yellow bell peppers.

PER SERVING (1 stuffed pita): 320 Cal, 9 g Fat, 2 g Sat Fat, 0 g Trans Fat, 4 mg Chol, 749 mg Sod, 50 g Carb, 9 g Fib, 14 g Prot, 142 mg Calc. *POINTS* value: **6.**

CALIFORNIA VEGGIE SANDWICHES WITH HORSERADISH

PREP 15 MIN • **COOK** NONE • **SERVES** 4

¼ cup fat-free mayonnaise

1 teaspoon prepared horseradish

8 thin slices 12-grain bread, lightly toasted

4 lettuce leaves

1 large tomato, sliced

1 small avocado, peeled, pitted, and sliced

2 thin slices red onion, separated into rings

1 large carrot, shredded

3 ounces (4 slices) reduced-fat deli Swiss or cheddar cheese

1 Stir the mayonnaise and horseradish together in a small bowl.

2 Spread the bread slices evenly with the mayonnaise mixture. Layer the lettuce, tomato, avocado, onion, carrot, and cheese over 4 slices of the bread and top each with a slice of the remaining bread. Cut each sandwich in half and serve at once. Or wrap in plastic wrap and refrigerate up to 6 hours.

PER SERVING (1 sandwich): 239 Cal, 9 g Fat, 2 g Sat Fat, 0 g Trans Fat, 9 mg Chol, 441 mg Sod, 29 g Carb, 7 g Fib, 13 g Prot, 274 mg Calc. **POINTS** value: **5.**

ASIAN CHICKEN-AND-RICE SOUP

PREP 15 MIN • **COOK** 25 MIN • **SERVES** 4

2   cups water
¼   cup quick-cooking brown rice
1   (14-ounce) can reduced-sodium chicken broth
1   (8-ounce) container sliced cremini mushrooms
4   cups baby spinach
1   cup shredded cooked chicken breast

1   carrot, shredded
3   scallions, sliced
2   tablespoons reduced-sodium soy sauce
2   teaspoons grated peeled fresh ginger
1   teaspoon Asian (dark) sesame oil

1 Combine the water and rice in a large saucepan and bring to a boil. Stir in the broth and mushrooms and return to a boil. Reduce the heat and simmer, covered, until the rice is tender, about 10 minutes.

2 Add the spinach, chicken, carrot, scallions, soy sauce, and ginger; simmer, covered, until the vegetables are tender, 8 minutes. Stir in the sesame oil and serve at once. Or transfer to individual microwave-safe containers and let cool. Cover and refrigerate up to 3 days. To reheat, microwave each 1-cup serving on High until heated through, 2 minutes.

> **◗ Filling Extra**
> Double the amount of carrot and scallions in the recipe.

PER SERVING (1 cup): 137 Cal, 3 g Fat, 1 g Sat Fat, 0 g Trans Fat, 29 mg Chol, 623 mg Sod, 12 g Carb, 3 g Fib, 15 g Prot, 74 mg Calc. *POINTS* value: **2.**

WHITE BEAN–AND-SAUSAGE SOUP WITH ESCAROLE

PREP 15 MIN • COOK 40 MIN • SERVES 4

2   links (7 ounces total) Italian turkey sausage, casings removed

1   small onion, chopped

1   carrot, chopped

1   celery stalk, chopped

2   garlic cloves, minced

2   cups water

1   ($15^1/_2$-ounce) can cannellini (white kidney) beans, rinsed and drained

1   (14-ounce) can reduced-sodium chicken broth

$^1/_2$ head escarole, cut into 2-inch pieces (4 cups)

1 Spray a Dutch oven or large saucepan with nonstick spray and set over medium-high heat. Add the sausage, onion, carrot, and celery and cook, stirring frequently to break up the sausage, until the sausage is no longer pink, 8 minutes. Stir in the garlic and cook for 1 minute.

2 Add the water, beans, and broth; bring to a boil. Reduce the heat and simmer, covered, for 10 minutes. Stir in the escarole and simmer, covered, until the escarole is tender, 15 minutes. Serve at once. Or transfer to individual microwave-safe containers and let cool. Cover and refrigerate up to 3 days. To reheat, microwave each 1-cup serving on High until heated through, 2 minutes.

▶ Filling Extra

Add 2 medium chopped tomatoes or a $14^1/_2$-ounce can of diced tomatoes when you add the escarole.

PER SERVING (1 generous cup): 230 Cal, 6 g Fat, 1 g Sat Fat, 0 g Trans Fat, 46 mg Chol, 820 mg Sod, 24 g Carb, 7 g Fib, 21 g Prot, 120 mg Calc. **POINTS** value: **4.**

SPICY CHICKEN
TORTILLA SOUP

SPICY CHICKEN TORTILLA SOUP

PREP 15 MIN • **COOK** 20 MIN • **SERVES** 4

1 (14½-ounce) can diced tomatoes with mild green chiles

1 (14-ounce) can reduced-sodium chicken broth

2 cups thawed frozen mixed vegetables (broccoli, cauliflower, carrots, corn, and red bell pepper)

1 cup water

2 teaspoons ground cumin

1 cup chopped cooked chicken breast

3 tablespoons chopped fresh cilantro

1 tablespoon lime juice

12 baked tortilla chips, crumbled

1 Combine the tomatoes, broth, vegetables, water, and cumin in a large saucepan and bring to a boil. Reduce the heat and simmer, covered, until the vegetables are tender, 10 minutes.

2 Stir in the chicken and cook until heated through, 2 minutes. Stir in the cilantro and lime juice. Top each serving with 3 of the tortilla chips and serve at once. Or omit the tortilla chips and transfer to individual microwave-safe containers. Let cool, cover, and refrigerate up to 3 days. To reheat, microwave each 1¼-cup serving on High until heated through, 2 minutes. Top with the tortilla chips just before eating.

PER SERVING (1¼ cups soup with 3 tortilla chips): 170 Cal, 3 g Fat, 1 g Sat Fat, 0 g Trans Fat, 29 mg Chol, 712 mg Sod, 23 g Carb, 3 g Fib, 15 g Prot, 56 mg Calc. *POINTS* value: *3.*

CHUNKY SUMMER VEGETABLE SOUP

PREP 20 MIN • **COOK** 30 MIN • **SERVES** 4

2   teaspoons olive oil
1   onion, chopped
1½ cups water
2   large tomatoes, coarsely chopped
1   yellow squash, coarsely chopped

1   zucchini, coarsely chopped
1   red or yellow bell pepper, coarsely chopped
2   garlic cloves, minced
1   teaspoon salt
¼ teaspoon fennel seeds

1 Heat the oil in a Dutch oven or large saucepan over medium-high heat. Add the onion and cook, stirring occasionally, until lightly browned, about 6 minutes. Add the water, tomatoes, crookneck squash, zucchini, bell pepper, garlic, salt, and fennel seeds. Bring to a boil; reduce the heat and simmer, covered, until the vegetables are tender, about 20 minutes.

2 Let cool about 5 minutes. Puree 1½ cups of the soup in a blender or food processor. Stir the puree into the soup and serve at once. Or transfer to individual microwave-safe containers and let cool. Cover and refrigerate up to 3 days. To reheat, microwave each 1¼-cup serving on High until heated through, 2 minutes. The soup may also be served chilled.

◗ Filling Extra
To add color and bulk, use 1 red and 1 yellow bell pepper. This recipe works with the **Simply Filling technique.**

PER SERVING (1¼ cups): 75 Cal, 3 g Fat, 0 g Sat Fat, 0 g Trans Fat, 0 mg Chol, 606 mg Sod, 12 g Carb, 3 g Fib, 3 g Prot, 39 mg Calc. **POINTS** value: **1.**

CHICKEN-PECAN SALAD WITH GREENS AND GRAPES

PREP 20 MIN • COOK NONE • SERVES 4

¼ cup fat-free mayonnaise

1½ teaspoons Dijon mustard

1½ teaspoons red-wine vinegar

⅛ teaspoon salt

⅛ teaspoon black pepper

1 navel orange

2 cups shredded cooked chicken breast (8 ounces)

1 celery stalk, thinly sliced

2 scallions, thinly sliced

2 tablespoons chopped pecans, toasted

2 cups mixed fresh baby salad greens

1 cup seedless grapes, halved

1 Stir together the mayonnaise, mustard, vinegar, salt, and pepper in a large bowl. Grate ½ teaspoon zest from the orange and stir into the mayonnaise mixture. Remove the peel and white pith from the orange. Slice the orange and cut the slices into quarters.

2 Add the orange pieces, chicken, celery, scallions, and pecans to the mayonnaise mixture and stir to combine. Spoon the chicken salad over the salad greens, sprinkle with the grapes, and serve at once. If packing the salads for lunch, store servings of the chicken salad, greens, and grapes in separate containers for up to 24 hours and assemble just before eating.

◊ **Filling Extra**
For a heartier salad, stir 1 cup cooked barley or 1 cup cooked brown rice into the chicken salad. The per-serving **POINTS** value will increase by **1.**

PER SERVING (¾ cup chicken salad, ½ cup baby greens, ¼ cup grapes): 183 Cal, 6 g Fat, 1 g Sat Fat, 0 g Trans Fat, 50 mg Chol, 394 mg Sod, 15 g Carb, 3 g Fib, 19 g Prot, 53 mg Calc. **POINTS** value: **4.**

Antipasto Pasta Salad

6   ounces whole-wheat rotini (about 2 cups)

4   ounces green beans, trimmed and cut into 1-inch pieces

2   cups grape or cherry tomatoes, halved

1   (6$\frac{1}{2}$-ounce) jar marinated artichokes, drained

$\frac{1}{3}$ cup chopped roasted red bell pepper

1   celery stalk, chopped

4   ounces part-skim mozzarella, cut into small cubes

3   ounces turkey salami, cut into thin strips

$\frac{1}{3}$ cup fat-free Italian salad dressing

3   tablespoons grated Parmesan

1 Cook the pasta according to the package directions, omitting the salt if desired and adding the green beans during the last 5 minutes of cooking time. Drain and rinse under cold running water.

2 Transfer the pasta and green beans to a large bowl. Add the tomatoes, artichokes, bell pepper, celery, mozzarella, salami, salad dressing, and Parmesan; stir to combine. Serve at once, or cover and refrigerate up to 2 days.

◗ Filling Extra
Serve the salad on a bed of fresh spinach or salad greens and garnish each plate with cucumber slices.

PER SERVING (1$\frac{1}{3}$ cups): 227 Cal, 7 g Fat, 4 g Sat Fat, 0 g Trans Fat, 20 mg Chol, 610 mg Sod, 29 g Carb, 6 g Fib, 14 g Prot, 217 mg Calc. **POINTS** value: **4.**

LEMONY TUNA-AND–WHITE BEAN SALAD

PREP 15 MIN • **COOK** NONE • **SERVES** 4

1   (15½-ounce) can small white beans, rinsed and drained

1   (6-ounce) can solid white tuna in water, drained and flaked

1   tomato, cut into bite-size pieces

1   celery stalk, diced

2   tablespoons diced red onion

½   teaspoon grated lemon zest

2   tablespoons lemon juice

1   teaspoon extra-virgin olive oil

⅛   teaspoon salt

⅛   teaspoon black pepper

> **♦ Filling Extra**
> Serve each salad with 1 cup fresh orange sections and increase the **POINTS** value by **1.** This recipe works with the **Simply Filling technique.**

Place all the ingredients in a large bowl and toss to combine. Let stand 10 minutes to allow the flavors to blend. Serve at once, or cover and refrigerate up to 3 days.

PER SERVING (generous ¾ cup): 169 Cal, 2 g Fat, 0 g Sat Fat, 0 g Trans Fat, 12 mg Chol, 442 mg Sod, 21 g Carb, 5 g Fib, 18 g Prot, 81 mg Calc. **POINTS** value: **3.**

SOUTH-OF-THE-BORDER SHRIMP-AND–BLACK BEAN SALAD

PREP 20 MIN • **COOK** 15 MIN • **SERVES** 4

³/4 cup water

¹/4 cup quick-cooking brown rice

1 cup fresh or thawed frozen corn kernels

2 tablespoons cider vinegar

1 teaspoon olive oil

¹/2 teaspoon chili powder

¹/4 teaspoon salt

1 (15¹/2-ounce) can black beans, rinsed and drained

8 ounces cooked medium shrimp, halved lengthwise

1 tomato, cut into bite-size pieces

2 scallions, sliced

1 Combine the water and rice in a medium saucepan and bring to a boil. Reduce the heat, cover, and simmer 5 minutes. Stir in the corn and simmer, covered, until the water is absorbed and the rice is tender, 7 minutes. Transfer to a shallow bowl and let cool 10 minutes.

2 Whisk the vinegar, oil, chili powder, and salt together in a large bowl. Add the rice mixture, beans, shrimp, tomato, and scallions; stir to combine. Serve at once, or cover and refrigerate up to 2 days.

In the Kitchen
If you refrigerate the salad, let it stand on the counter about 15 minutes before serving. This recipe works with the **Simply Filling technique.**

PER SERVING (1¹/3 cups): 234 Cal, 3 g Fat, 0 g Sat Fat, 0 g Trans Fat, 111 mg Chol, 571 mg Sod, 33 g Carb, 10 g Fib, 20 g Prot, 88 mg Calc. *POINTS* value: **4.**

MEDITERRANEAN CHICKPEA SALAD WITH LEMON DRESSING

PREP 15 MIN • COOK NONE • SERVES 4

2   tablespoons lemon juice

1   tablespoon olive oil

1   garlic clove, minced

1/2 teaspoon dried oregano

1/4 teaspoon salt

1/4 teaspoon black pepper

1   small head romaine lettuce, torn into bite-size pieces (about 6 cups)

1   medium English (seedless) cucumber, peeled and diced

2   cups cherry tomatoes, halved

1   (15 1/2-ounce) can chickpeas, rinsed and drained

1   (7-ounce) jar roasted red peppers, drained and thinly sliced

1   (6 1/2-ounce) jar artichoke hearts, drained and quartered

1/2 cup crumbled reduced-fat feta

6   pitted kalamata olives, coarsely chopped

1 Whisk the lemon juice, oil, garlic, oregano, salt, and pepper together in a small bowl.

2 Arrange the lettuce on a large platter; top with the cucumber, tomatoes, chickpeas, peppers, and artichoke hearts. Drizzle with the dressing and sprinkle with the cheese and olives. Serve at once, or cover and refrigerate up to 3 days.

◊ Filling Extra

Add more flavor and crunch by topping the salad with 1 small thinly sliced red onion.

PER SERVING (about 2 cups): 287 Cal, 11 g Fat, 4 g Sat Fat, 0 g Trans Fat, 17 mg Chol, 700 mg Sod, 38 g Carb, 13 g Fib, 14 g Prot, 212 mg Calc. *POINTS* value: **6.**

EDAMAME-PEANUT NOODLE SALAD

PREP 20 MIN • **COOK** 15 MIN • **SERVES** 6

6 ounces whole-wheat linguine

1 cup thawed frozen shelled edamame
(green soybeans)

3 tablespoons low-sodium soy sauce

3 tablespoons natural peanut butter

2 tablespoons rice vinegar

1 tablespoon honey

2 teaspoons grated peeled fresh ginger

1½ teaspoons Asian (dark) sesame oil

1 garlic clove, minced

⅛ teaspoon red pepper flakes

3 scallions, sliced

1 large carrot, shredded

1 red bell pepper, very thinly sliced

½ English cucumber, thinly sliced

1 Cook the pasta according to the package directions, omitting the salt if desired and adding the edamame during the last 5 minutes of cooking time. Drain and rinse under cold running water.

2 Whisk the soy sauce, peanut butter, vinegar, honey, ginger, sesame oil, garlic, and pepper flakes in a large bowl until blended. Add the pasta mixture, scallions, carrot, bell pepper, and cucumber; toss to coat. Serve at once, or cover and refrigerate up to 1 day.

In the Kitchen
Natural peanut butter, once available only in health food stores, can now be found in almost any supermarket. It's made with no added sugar or oil.

PER SERVING (generous 1 cup): 227 Cal, 7 g Fat, 1 g Sat Fat, 0 g Trans Fat, 0 mg Chol, 421 mg Sod, 34 g Carb, 5 g Fib, 10 g Prot, 51 mg Calc. *POINTS* value: *4.*

EDAMAME-PEANUT
NOODLE SALAD

FAVORITE
MUNCHIES AND
LIGHT BITES

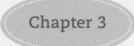

Chapter 3

Chunky Avocado Guacamole

PREP 20 MIN • COOK 8 MIN • SERVES 8

1 cup thawed frozen shelled edamame (green soybeans)

3 tablespoons lime juice

3 tablespoons fat-free mayonnaise

1 medium Hass avocado, halved, pitted, and peeled

1 large plum tomato, chopped

1/2 small red onion, finely chopped

2 tablespoons chopped fresh cilantro

1 tablespoon minced pickled jalapeño pepper

1/2 teaspoon ground cumin

1/2 teaspoon salt

1 Cook the edamame according to the package directions; drain.

2 Let the edamame cool for 5 minutes. Put in a food processor and puree, scraping the sides of the bowl frequently, until completely smooth, about 3 minutes. Add the lime juice and mayonnaise and pulse until blended.

3 Mash the avocado with a fork in a medium bowl until chunky. Stir in the edamame mixture, tomato, onion, cilantro, jalapeño, cumin, and salt. Press a piece of plastic wrap directly onto the surface to prevent the guacamole from browning. Refrigerate until well chilled, at least 2 hours or up to 4 hours.

> **Filling Extra**
> Instead of serving this dip with the usual tortilla chips, serve it with colorful strips of yellow and red bell peppers. This recipe works with the **Simply Filling technique.**

PER SERVING (1/4 cup): 61 Cal, 4 g Fat, 1 g Sat Fat, 0 g Trans Fat, 1 mg Chol, 197 mg Sod, 5 g Carb, 3 g Fib, 3 g Prot, 19 mg Calc. *POINTS* value: *1.*

CARAMELIZED ONION DIP

PREP 20 MIN • COOK 30 MIN • SERVES 8

2   teaspoons olive oil
1   large sweet onion, finely chopped
3   shallots, thinly sliced
¼   cup water
1   beef bouillon cube
1   cup light sour cream

⅓   cup light mayonnaise
2   teaspoons lemon juice
⅛   teaspoon salt
4   cups assorted vegetables (such as carrots, celery, and bell peppers), cut up

1 Heat the oil in a large skillet over medium heat. Add the onion and shallots. Cover and cook, stirring occasionally, until the onions are softened, 5 minutes. Reduce the heat to medium-low, uncover, and cook, stirring frequently, until the onions are very soft and golden brown, 20 to 25 minutes. Spoon the onion mixture onto a plate. Add the water to the skillet and crumble in the bouillon cube, stirring until the bouillon dissolves. Let the onions and the broth stand until cool, 20 minutes.

In the Kitchen
If the dip is too thick after refrigerating, stir in 1 to 2 tablespoons water.

2 Stir together the onion mixture, broth, sour cream, mayonnaise, lemon juice, and salt in a medium bowl. Cover and refrigerate at least 2 hours or overnight to allow the flavors to blend. Serve the dip with the vegetables.

PER SERVING (¼ cup dip with ½ cup vegetables): 116 Cal, 8 g Fat, 3 g Sat Fat, 0 g Trans Fat, 15 mg Chol, 300 mg Sod, 10 g Carb, 2 g Fib, 2 g Prot, 57 mg Calc. *POINTS* value: **3.**

WARM CHEESE, SPINACH, AND ARTICHOKE DIP

PREP 25 MIN • **COOK/BAKE** 35 MIN • **SERVES** 16

1 teaspoon olive oil

1 medium onion, finely chopped

3 garlic cloves, minced

1 (14-ounce) can artichoke hearts, drained

½ cup roasted red bell peppers, rinsed

4 ounces fat-free cream cheese, cut into 4 pieces

½ cup light sour cream

4 tablespoons grated Parmesan

2 tablespoons light mayonnaise

1 (10-ounce) package frozen chopped spinach, thawed and squeezed dry

⅓ cup shredded part-skim mozzarella

½ teaspoon salt

8 cups assorted vegetable sticks

1 Preheat the oven to 350°F. Spray a 9-inch pie plate with nonstick spray.

2 Heat the oil in a large nonstick skillet over medium heat. Add the onion and cook, stirring occasionally, until the onion is lightly browned, 6 minutes. Stir in the garlic and cook, stirring frequently, for 2 minutes.

3 Put the artichokes and red peppers in a food processor and pulse until coarsely chopped. Add the cream cheese, sour cream, 3 tablespoons of the Parmesan, and mayonnaise; pulse until blended.

In the Kitchen
Bake the dip in 2 (2-cup) ovenproof baking dishes instead of a pie plate if you wish.

4 Stir the spinach into the onion mixture in the skillet. Then stir in the artichoke mixture, mozzarella, and salt. Spoon the mixture into the pie plate and spread evenly with a spatula. Sprinkle with the remaining 1 tablespoon Parmesan.

5 Bake until heated through and the cheese is melted, 25–30 minutes. Serve at once with the vegetables for dipping.

PER SERVING (¼ cup dip and ½ cup vegetables): 79 Cal, 3 g Fat, 1 g Sat Fat, 0 g Trans Fat, 7 mg Chol, 264 mg Sod, 9 g Carb, 4 g Fib, 4 g Prot, 97 mg Calc. *POINTS* value: *1.*

WARM CHEESE, SPINACH,
AND ARTICHOKE DIP

WHITE BEAN–BASIL DIP WITH GRILLED VEGETABLES

PREP 20 MIN • COOK 15 MIN • SERVES 8

1   tablespoon olive oil

2   garlic cloves, minced

$1/8$ teaspoon red pepper flakes

2   plum tomatoes, finely chopped

1   (15$1/2$-ounce) can cannellini (white kidney) beans, rinsed and drained

$1/4$ cup plain fat-free Greek yogurt

$1/4$ cup fresh basil leaves

1   tablespoon lemon juice

1   teaspoon grated lemon zest

$1/2$ teaspoon salt

1   pound asparagus, trimmed

1   large red bell pepper, cut into 1-inch strips

1   fennel bulb, halved lengthwise and sliced

1 Heat the oil in a medium skillet over medium-low heat. Add the garlic and pepper flakes and cook, stirring constantly, until the garlic is just golden, about 1 minute. Add the tomatoes and cook, stirring occasionally, until softened, 3 minutes.

2 Put the beans in a food processor and puree, scraping the sides of the bowl frequently, until completely smooth, 3 minutes. Add the yogurt, basil, lemon juice, lemon zest, and salt and pulse until blended. Add the tomato mixture and pulse just until blended. Spoon the dip into a bowl.

In the Kitchen
If you don't have time to grill the vegetables, serve the dip with cut-up raw vegetables that you have on hand. This recipe works with the **Simply Filling technique.**

3 Spray a nonstick ridged grill pan with olive oil nonstick spray and set over medium-high heat. Place the vegetables in the pan in batches, and grill, turning often, until lightly browned and crisp-tender, 8–10 minutes. Transfer the vegetables to a platter and serve with the dip.

PER SERVING ($1/4$ cup dip with about $1/2$ cup vegetables): 97 Cal, 2 g Fat, 0 g Sat Fat, 0 g Trans Fat, 0 mg Chol, 286 mg Sod, 15 g Carb, 5 g Fib, 6 g Prot, 78 mg Calc. *POINTS* value: **1.**

CRUNCHY BEAN-AND-CHEESE NACHO CUPS

PREP 25 MIN • **MICROWAVE/BAKE** 10 MIN • **SERVES** 10

1 plum tomato, seeded and finely chopped

¼ cup salsa

3 tablespoons fat-free sour cream

1 tablespoon chopped fresh cilantro

1 teaspoon lime juice

¼ teaspoon ground cumin

1 cup fat-free spicy refried beans

40 baked cup-shaped tortilla chips (about 2 ounces)

1¼ cups shredded reduced-fat Mexican cheese blend

2 scallions, chopped

1 Preheat the oven to 400°F. Spray a large baking sheet with nonstick spray.

2 Stir together the tomato and the salsa in a small bowl. Stir together the sour cream, cilantro, lime juice, and cumin in another small bowl.

3 Place the beans in a microwavable bowl, cover with plastic wrap, and prick a few holes in the plastic. Microwave on High until hot, 2 minutes, stirring once halfway through cooking. Spoon about 1 teaspoon of the beans into each tortilla cup; sprinkle evenly with the cheese and scallions.

4 Place the tortilla cups on the baking sheet and bake until the cheese is melted, 5 minutes. Top each cup evenly with the tomato mixture, then with the sour cream mixture.

In the Kitchen

If you can't find fat-free spicy refried beans, stir a few dashes of hot sauce into plain fat-free refried beans.

PER SERVING (4 nacho cups): 107 Cal, 4 g Fat, 2 g Sat Fat, 0 g Trans Fat, 8 mg Chol, 293 mg Sod, 14 g Carb, 2 g Fib, 5 g Prot, 159 mg Calc. *POINTS* value: *2.*

MINI REUBEN SNACK
SANDWICHES

MINI REUBEN SNACK SANDWICHES

PREP 15 MIN • COOK 10 MIN • SERVES 8

2 cups coleslaw mix
1/4 cup water
1 tablespoon cider vinegar
16 slices mini cocktail rye bread
3 tablespoons light Thousand Island salad dressing

4 thin slices reduced-fat Swiss cheese, cut into quarters
4 ounces very thinly sliced lean deli corned beef

1 Combine the coleslaw mix, water, and vinegar in a small skillet. Bring to a boil over medium-high heat. Reduce the heat to medium-low and cook, stirring occasionally, until the cabbage wilts and all of the water evaporates, 5 minutes. Let cool.

2 Spread the dressing evenly on each slice of the bread. Top 8 of the bread slices with a piece of the cheese. Top evenly with the corned beef, coleslaw mixture, and remaining cheese slices. Top with a slice of the remaining bread.

In the Kitchen

If you don't have a cast iron skillet for pressing the sandwiches, use a regular skillet and place a couple of heavy cans inside the skillet for added weight.

3 Lightly spray a large nonstick skillet with nonstick spray and set over medium heat. Add the sandwiches, in batches, if necessary, and top with a heavy weight, such as a cast iron skillet. Cook until the bread is lightly browned and crisp, 2 minutes. With a spatula, turn the sandwiches, weigh them down, and cook until the other sides are browned, 2 minutes. Cut each sandwich in half.

PER SERVING (2 sandwich halves): 88 Cal, 2 g Fat, 1 g Sat Fat, 0 g Trans Fat, 10 mg Chol, 327 mg Sod, 10 g Carb, 1 g Fib, 7 g Prot, 120 mg Calc. *POINTS* value: *2.*

CREAMY CRAB CROSTINI

1   (6-ounce) can lump crabmeat, drained
1/3 cup light mayonnaise
1/4 cup fat-free Greek yogurt
1/4 cup grated Parmesan

1   tablespoon chopped fresh chives
1/2 teaspoon grated lemon zest
Pinch salt
36 (1/4-inch-thick) slices French baguette

1 Preheat the oven to 400°F. Spray a large baking sheet with nonstick spray.

2 Stir together the crabmeat, mayonnaise, yogurt, Parmesan, chives, lemon zest, and salt in a medium bowl. Spread 1 slightly rounded teaspoon of the crab mixture on each baguette slice and place on the prepared baking sheet.

3 Bake until the crostini are lightly browned, 10–12 minutes.

PER SERVING (3 crostini): 83 Cal, 3 g Fat, 1 g Sat Fat, 0 g Trans Fat, 16 mg Chol, 245 mg Sod, 8 g Carb, 0 g Fib, 6 g Prot, 59 mg Calc. *POINTS* value: **2.**

SESAME CHEESE CRISPS

PREP 25 MIN • BAKE 10 MIN • MAKES 40

$1/2$ cup all-purpose flour

$1/4$ cup cornmeal

$1/4$ teaspoon baking soda

$1/8$ teaspoon cayenne

$1/8$ teaspoon salt

$3/4$ cup shredded reduced-fat sharp cheddar

$1/4$ cup grated Parmesan

4 tablespoons light butter, cut up and softened

2 teaspoons water

$1 1/2$ teaspoons sesame seeds

1 Adjust the racks to divide the oven into thirds and preheat the oven to 350°F. Spray 2 baking sheets with nonstick spray.

2 Put the flour, cornmeal, baking soda, cayenne, and salt in a food processor; pulse until blended. Add the cheddar, Parmesan, and butter; pulse until the mixture resembles coarse crumbs. Add 1 teaspoon of the water through the feed tube, pulsing just until a dough forms and adding the remaining 1 teaspoon water if necessary. Turn the dough out onto a work surface and gather into a ball.

3 Roll scant teaspoons of the dough into $3/4$-inch balls, making a total of 40 balls. Place on the baking sheets about 2 inches apart, then press with a glass dipped in flour to make $1 3/4$-inch rounds. With a fork, press a checkerboard design into the top of each one. Sprinkle evenly with the sesame seeds.

4 Bake until lightly browned at the edges, 10–12 minutes, rotating the baking sheets halfway through the baking. Let cool on the baking sheets on racks for 1 minute. With a spatula, transfer the crisps to racks and let cool completely. Store in an airtight container at room temperature for up to 1 week.

PER SERVING (2 crisps): 43 Cal, 2 g Fat, 1 g Sat Fat, 0 g Trans Fat, 5 mg Chol, 107 mg Sod, 4 g Carb, 0 g Fib, 2 g Prot, 48 mg Calc. **POINTS** value: **1.**

FOUR-CHEESE PEPPERONI-VEGETABLE PIZZA

PREP 30 MIN • COOK/BAKE 25 MIN • SERVES 12

1   medium onion, halved and thinly sliced

1   red bell pepper, thinly sliced

8   ounces white mushrooms, sliced

1   cup grape tomatoes, halved

1   pound refrigerated or thawed frozen pizza dough, at room temperature

$^3/_4$ cup fat-free marinara sauce

$1^1/_2$ cups shredded reduced-fat Italian four-cheese blend

2   tablespoons grated Parmesan

36   slices turkey pepperoni

1 Adjust the oven racks to divide the oven in thirds and preheat the oven to 450°F. Spray a $10^1/_2$ x $15^1/_2$ -inch jelly-roll pan with nonstick spray.

2 Spray a large nonstick skillet with nonstick spray and set over medium-high heat. Add the onion, bell pepper, and mushrooms. Cook, stirring occasionally, until the vegetables are tender and the liquid has evaporated, 8–10 minutes. Stir in the tomatoes and cook 1 minute.

In the Kitchen
Add 1 cup of sliced zucchini or broccoli florets, cooking them along with the other vegetables.

3 With floured hands, press the dough over the bottom of the prepared pan. If the dough shrinks back, let it rest a few minutes before pressing again. Spread the marinara sauce evenly over the dough. Sprinkle with $^1/_2$ cup of the cheese blend and 1 tablespoon of the Parmesan. Top evenly with the onion mixture and the pepperoni.

4 Bake on the lowest oven rack until the crust is browned on the bottom, 12–15 minutes. Sprinkle with the remaining 1 cup shredded cheese blend and 1 tablespoon Parmesan. Bake until the cheese melts, 4–5 minutes longer. Cut into 24 squares.

PER SERVING (2 squares): 190 Cal, 7 g Fat, 3 g Sat Fat, 0 g Trans Fat, 23 mg Chol, 641 mg Sod, 21 g Carb, 2 g Fib, 11 g Prot, 170 mg Calc. *POINTS* value: **4.**

FOUR-CHEESE
PEPPERONI-VEGETABLE
PIZZA

MINI HAM-AND-CHEDDAR QUICHES

PREP 10 MIN • BAKE 12 MIN • SERVES 15

1 ounce low-sodium ham, chopped

$^1/_4$ cup shredded fat-free cheddar

1 (1.9-ounce) box thawed frozen mini phyllo pastry shells (15 shells)

2 tablespoons fat-free egg substitute

2 tablespoons fat-free half-and-half

$^1/_4$ teaspoon Dijon mustard

Pinch salt

1 Preheat the oven to 350°F.

2 Sprinkle the ham and cheese evenly into the pastry shells. Whisk together the egg substitute, half-and-half, mustard, and salt in a small bowl. Spoon the egg mixture evenly into the shells.

3 Place the pastry shells on a baking sheet and bake until the pastry is lightly crisped and the filling is set, 12–15 minutes.

PER SERVING (1 quiche): 26 Cal, 1 g Fat, 0 g Sat Fat, 0 g Trans Fat, 1 mg Chol, 79 mg Sod, 3 g Carb, 0 g Fib, 1 g Prot, 22 mg Calc. **POINTS** value: **1.**

BBQ Turkey, Corn, and Mango Quesadillas

PREP 15 MIN • COOK 15 MIN • SERVES 6

1 small red onion, halved and thinly sliced
1/2 cup fresh or thawed frozen corn kernels
6 ounces thin-sliced deli turkey breast, cut into thin strips
2 tablespoons barbecue sauce

3/4 cup shredded reduced-fat pepperjack
4 (8-inch) whole-wheat tortillas
1 mango, peeled, pitted, and sliced
2 tablespoons chopped cilantro

1 Spray a large nonstick skillet with nonstick spray and set over medium heat. Add the onion and cook, stirring occasionally, until softened, 5 minutes. Stir in the corn and cook 2 minutes.

2 Place the turkey and barbecue sauce in a medium bowl and toss to coat.

3 Sprinkle half of the cheese on 2 of the tortillas, then top evenly with all of the turkey mixture, onion mixture, mango, cilantro, and the remaining half of the cheese. Top with the remaining 2 tortillas, lightly pressing down on each stack.

4 Wipe the skillet clean, spray with nonstick spray, and set over medium heat. Add one of the tortilla stacks and cook until lightly browned and heated through, 2–3 minutes on each side. Transfer the quesadilla to a cutting board and keep warm. Repeat with the remaining tortilla stack. Cut each quesadilla into 6 wedges.

In the Kitchen

If you can't find reduced-fat pepperjack cheese, use reduced-fat Monterey Jack and add a seeded and minced fresh or pickled jalapeño to the quesadillas.

PER SERVING (2 wedges): 178 Cal, 5 g Fat, 2 g Sat Fat, 0 g Trans Fat, 23 mg Chol, 637 mg Sod, 24 g Carb, 3 g Fib, 11 g Prot, 118 mg Calc. *POINTS* value: *3.*

FROM TOP, CLOCKWISE:

HOT 'N' SMOKY SNACK MIX, PAGE 71,

CRUNCHY BEAN-AND- CHEESE NACHO CUPS, PAGE 59,

AND BLAZIN' BUFFALO CHICKEN BITES WITH BLUE CHEESE DIP

BLAZIN' BUFFALO CHICKEN BITES WITH BLUE CHEESE DIP

PREP 15 MIN • COOK 10 MIN • SERVES 8

1/2 cup light sour cream

1/4 cup crumbled reduced-fat blue cheese

3 tablespoons light mayonnaise

2 tablespoons fat-free milk

1 teaspoon lemon juice

1/8 teaspoon salt

1 1/4 pounds chicken tenders, cut into 1 1/2-inch pieces

3 tablespoons cayenne pepper sauce

1 tablespoon honey

1 tablespoon water

2 teaspoons Dijon mustard

2 cups carrot sticks

2 cups celery sticks

1 To make the dip, stir together the sour cream, blue cheese, mayonnaise, milk, lemon juice, and salt. Cover and refrigerate to allow the flavors to blend, 15 minutes.

2 Spray a large nonstick skillet with nonstick spray and set over medium-high heat. Add the chicken and cook until browned and cooked through, 3–4 minutes on each side. Transfer to a platter and keep warm.

3 Add the pepper sauce, honey, water, and mustard to the skillet and cook over medium heat, stirring constantly, until the mixture comes to a boil, 1 minute. Drizzle the sauce mixture over the chicken. Serve with the dip and the carrot and celery sticks.

In the Kitchen

Cayenne pepper sauce is a less spicy variety of hot sauce. To make the chicken even milder, reduce the pepper sauce to 2 tablespoons and add an additional tablespoon of water.

PER SERVING (5 pieces chicken, about 2 tablespoons dip, and 1/2 cup carrot and celery sticks): 157 Cal, 7 g Fat, 3 g Sat Fat, 0 g Trans Fat, 54 mg Chol, 375 mg Sod, 5 g Carb, 1 g Fib, 18 g Prot, 62 mg Calc. *POINTS* value: **4.**

GRILLED SHRIMP WITH ZESTY LIME SAUCE

PREP 15 MIN • **COOK** 5 MIN • **SERVES** 6

1/2 cup cocktail sauce

2 tablespoons fat-free mayonnaise

1/2 teaspoon grated lime zest

1 tablespoon lime juice

3/4 teaspoon Cajun seasoning

24 large shrimp, peeled and deveined, tails left on if desired

1 teaspoon olive oil

1 Stir together the cocktail sauce, mayonnaise, lime zest, lime juice, and 1/4 teaspoon of the Cajun seasoning in a small bowl. Cover and refrigerate to allow the flavors to blend, 15 minutes.

2 Combine the shrimp, oil, and the remaining 1/2 teaspoon of the Cajun seasoning in a medium bowl and toss to coat. Thread the shrimp on 6 (8-inch) metal skewers.

3 Heat a stove-top grill pan over medium-high heat. Grill the shrimp, in batches if necessary, until the shrimp are just opaque in the center, 2–3 minutes on each side. Serve with the sauce.

> **Filling Extra**
> Serve the shrimp on a bed of mixed salad greens and drizzle with the sauce. This recipe works with the **Simply Filling technique.**

PER SERVING (4 shrimp with scant 2 tablespoons sauce): 57 Cal, 1 g Fat, 0 g Sat Fat, 0 g Trans Fat, 47 mg Chol, 415 mg Sod, 7 g Carb, 0 g Fib, 5 g Prot, 14 mg Calc. **POINTS** value: **1.**

Hot 'n' Smoky Snack Mix

PREP 10 MIN • BAKE 50 MIN • SERVES 24

6   cups fat-fee popped popcorn
3   cups crispy corn cereal squares
2   cups crispy wheat cereal squares
2   cups unsalted mini pretzel twists
1   cup whole grain cheddar fish-shaped crackers
3   tablespoons unsalted butter
2   tablespoons Worcestershire sauce

2   tablespoons packed brown sugar
2   teaspoons smoked paprika
1   teaspoon ground cumin
1/4 teaspoon cayenne
1/4 teaspoon salt
1/2 cup smoked almonds

1 Preheat the oven to 250°F. Spray a large shallow roasting pan with nonstick spray. Combine the popcorn, cereals, pretzels, and crackers in the roasting pan.

2 Combine the butter, Worcestershire sauce, and brown sugar in a small saucepan. Cook over low heat, stirring occasionally, until the butter is melted, 2 minutes. Stir in the paprika, cumin, cayenne, and salt. Drizzle the butter mixture over the cereal mixture, stirring as you drizzle; stir well to coat.

In the Kitchen
If you can't find smoked paprika, use regular paprika instead.

3 Bake until crisp, 45 minutes, stirring every 15 minutes. Stir in the almonds. Transfer the mixture to a baking sheet lined with wax paper to cool completely. Store in an airtight container up to 1 week.

PER SERVING (1/2 cup): 97 Cal, 4 g Fat, 1 g Sat Fat, 0 g Trans Fat, 4 mg Chol, 150 mg Sod, 15 g Carb, 1 g Fib, 2 g Prot, 37 mg Calc. *POINTS* value: *2.*

SATISFYING STEWS AND MORE

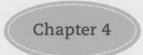

Chapter 4

CARIBBEAN BEEF STEW WITH COCONUT BASMATI RICE

PREP 15 MIN • **COOK** 1 HR 15 MIN • **SERVES** 6

1 pound lean boneless beef bottom round, cut into 1-inch chunks

1 tablespoon jerk seasoning

2 teaspoons olive oil

1 onion, thinly sliced

2 garlic cloves, minced

1 (14^1/$_2$-ounce) can diced tomatoes

1 (14^1/$_2$-ounce) reduced-sodium beef broth

2 sweet potatoes, peeled and cubed

^{1}/$_2$ pound fresh green beans, trimmed and cut into 1-inch pieces

2 cups water

1 cup brown basmati rice

^{1}/$_2$ cup light (reduced-fat) coconut milk

1 Sprinkle the beef with the seasoning. Heat the oil in a Dutch oven over medium-high heat. Add the beef and cook, stirring occasionally, until browned, 4 minutes. Add the onion and garlic and cook, stirring occasionally, until the onion is softened, about 5 minutes. Add the tomatoes and broth; bring to a boil. Reduce the heat and simmer, covered, until the beef is almost tender, 45 minutes. Add the potatoes and simmer, covered, until almost tender, 15 minutes. Add the beans and simmer, covered, until tender, about 6 minutes longer.

In the Kitchen

Make a double batch of this spicy stew and freeze it for up to 3 months. Thaw the stew in the refrigerator the night before you plan to serve it.

2 Meanwhile, to make the rice, bring the water to a boil in a medium saucepan. Add the rice and coconut milk; return to a boil. Reduce the heat and simmer, covered, until the rice is tender, about 40 minutes. Serve the stew with the rice.

PER SERVING (generous 1 cup stew with ^{1}/$_2$ cup rice): 344 Cal, 7 g Fat, 2 g Sat Fat, 0 g Trans Fat, 56 mg Chol, 206 mg Sod, 42 g Carb, 7 g Fib, 29 g Prot, 80 mg Calc. **POINTS** value: **7.**

PEASANT-STYLE PORK GOULASH

1   pound pork tenderloin, trimmed and cut into
    1-inch pieces
1/2 teaspoon salt
1/4 teaspoon black pepper
2   teaspoons olive oil
1   onion, thinly sliced

1   Golden Delicious apple, chopped
2   tomatoes, chopped
1   (1-pound) bag sauerkraut, rinsed and drained
1   (14 1/2-ounce) can reduced-sodium beef broth
2   tablespoons paprika
1   teaspoon caraway seeds

1 Sprinkle the pork with the salt and pepper. Heat 1 teaspoon of the oil in a Dutch oven over medium-high heat. Add the pork and cook, stirring often, until browned, 3–4 minutes. Transfer the pork to a plate.

2 Add the remaining 1 teaspoon oil to the Dutch oven. Add the onion and apple and cook, stirring occasionally, until tender, about 8 minutes. Add the tomatoes and cook, stirring occasionally, until the tomatoes are softened, 5 minutes. Add the sauerkraut, broth, paprika, and caraway seeds; bring to a boil. Reduce the heat and simmer, covered, until slightly thickened, 30 minutes.

> ▶ **Filling Extra**
> Serve this dish with whole-wheat rotini (3/4 cup of cooked whole-wheat rotini per serving will increase the **POINTS** value by **2**). This recipe works with the **Simply Filling technique.**

PER SERVING (generous 1 cup): 239 Cal, 8 g Fat, 2 g Sat Fat, 0 g Trans Fat, 48 mg Chol, 990 mg Sod, 18 g Carb, 6 g Fib, 27 g Prot, 61 mg Calc. **POINTS** value: **5.**

POWDER-KEG CHILI

PREP 10 MIN • **COOK** 35 MIN • **SERVES** 6

1 pound lean ground beef (5% fat or less)

1 onion, chopped

1 (28-ounce) can diced tomatoes

1 (15^1/$_2$-ounce) can pinto or kidney beans, rinsed and drained

1 (15-ounce) can tomato sauce

1 cup water

2 tablespoons chili powder

1 teaspoon ground cumin

^{1}/$_4$ teaspoon sugar

^{1}/$_4$ teaspoon cayenne

24 baked tortilla chips (optional)

1 Combine the beef and onion in a Dutch oven and cook over medium-high heat, breaking the beef apart with a wooden spoon, until the beef is browned, 5 minutes.

2 Add the tomatoes, beans, tomato sauce, water, chili powder, cumin, sugar, and cayenne. Bring to a boil; reduce the heat and simmer, partially covered, until thickened slightly, 30 minutes. Serve with tortilla chips, if using.

> ◗ **Filling Extra**
> Add a shredded carrot and a small diced zucchini along with the tomatoes in step 2.

PER SERVING (1 generous cup without tortilla chips): 214 Cal, 5 g Fat, 2 g Sat Fat, 0 g Trans Fat, 40 mg Chol, 738 mg Sod, 24 g Carb, 7 g Fib, 22 g Prot, 87 mg Calc. **POINTS** value: **4.**

POWDER-KEG CHILI

BALLYMALOE IRISH STEW

1 pound boneless lamb shoulder, trimmed and cut into 1-inch cubes

¹/₂ teaspoon salt

¹/₄ teaspoon black pepper

1 teaspoon olive oil

1 onion, chopped

2 tablespoons all-purpose flour

2 cups reduced-sodium beef broth

1 (14¹/₂-ounce) can diced tomatoes

²/₃ cup stout beer

2 russet potatoes, peeled and cut into 1-inch cubes

2 carrots, cut into 1-inch cubes

1 medium turnip, peeled and cut into 1-inch cubes

1 cup thawed frozen peas

1 Sprinkle the lamb with the salt and pepper. Heat the oil in a Dutch oven over medium-high heat. Add the onion and cook, stirring occasionally, until tender, about 5 minutes. Add the lamb and cook, turning occasionally, until browned, about 6 minutes. Stir in the flour; cook 1 minute.

2 Add the broth, tomatoes, and beer; bring to a boil. Reduce the heat and simmer, covered, until the lamb is almost tender, about 30 minutes. Add the potatoes, carrots, and turnip; bring to a boil. Reduce the heat and simmer, covered, until the vegetables are tender, about 25 minutes. Stir in the peas and cook until heated through, 2 minutes.

In the Kitchen
Stout is a type of dark ale and gives this stew a rich, roasted flavor. Substitute an equal amount of beef broth if you prefer not to use beer.

PER SERVING (1¹/₂ cups): 387 Cal, 10 g Fat, 3 g Sat Fat, 0 g Trans Fat, 81 mg Chol, 664 mg Sod, 39 g Carb, 6 g Fib, 33 g Prot, 87 mg Calc. *POINTS* value: *8.*

BRUNSWICK STEW

PREP 15 MIN • COOK 40 MIN • SERVES 4

1   tablespoon all-purpose flour

1/4 teaspoon cayenne

4   (5-ounce) skinless, boneless chicken breasts, each cut into 4 pieces

2   slices center-cut bacon

2   stalks celery, cut into 1/2-inch pieces

1   onion, halved and cut in 1-inch-thick slices

1   medium red bell pepper, cut into thick strips

1   (14 1/2-ounce) can diced tomatoes

1   cup thawed frozen mixed vegetables (corn, carrots, peas, and green beans)

1   tablespoon apple-cider vinegar

1/2 teaspoon Worcestershire sauce

1/8 teaspoon hot pepper sauce

1 Combine the flour and cayenne in a medium bowl. Add the chicken and toss to coat.

2 Cook the bacon in a large saucepan until crisp. Drain on paper towels and coarsely crumble. Add the chicken to the saucepan and cook until lightly browned, 2–3 minutes on each side. Transfer to a plate.

3 Add the celery, onion, and bell pepper to the saucepan; cook, stirring occasionally, until the vegetables are softened, 4–5 minutes. Stir in the chicken, bacon, tomatoes, mixed vegetables, vinegar, Worcestershire sauce, and pepper sauce; bring to a boil.

4 Reduce the heat and simmer, partially covered, until the vegetables are very tender and the stew is thickened, 20–25 minutes.

PER SERVING (1 1/2 cups): 268 Cal, 6 g Fat, 2 g Sat Fat, 0 g Trans Fat, 91 mg Chol, 337 mg Sod, 17 g Carb, 5 g Fib, 36 g Prot, 77 mg Calc. **POINTS** value: **5.**

OLD-FASHIONED CHICKEN
AND DUMPLINGS

Old-Fashioned Chicken and Dumplings

PREP 15 MIN • COOK 45 MIN • SERVES 4

2 teaspoons olive oil
3 celery stalks, chopped
2 carrots, chopped
1 onion, chopped
1 garlic clove, minced
1/4 teaspoon dried thyme
1 1/2 cups chopped cooked chicken breast
4 cups reduced-sodium chicken broth

1 bay leaf
1/4 cup chopped fresh parsley
1 cup all-purpose flour
1/2 teaspoon baking powder
1/4 teaspoon salt
1/8 teaspoon black pepper
1 cup water

1 Heat the oil in large saucepan over medium heat. Add the celery, carrots, onion, garlic, and thyme; cook, stirring occasionally, until the vegetables are softened, 5–6 minutes. Add the chicken, broth, and bay leaf and bring to a boil. Reduce the heat, cover, and simmer until the vegetables are tender, 20–25 minutes. Stir in the parsley.

2 Meanwhile, combine the flour, baking powder, salt, and pepper in a medium bowl. Stir the water into the flour mixture just until moistened. Drop the dough, by rounded teaspoonfuls, onto the simmering stew, making 12 dumplings. Cover and simmer until the dumplings have doubled in size and are cooked through, 15–20 minutes. Discard the bay leaf.

▶ **Filling Extra**
Add 1 cup frozen cut green beans during the last 10 minutes of cooking in step 1.

PER SERVING (1 1/2 cups chicken mixture and 3 dumplings): 269 Cal, 5 g Fat, 1 g Sat Fat, 0 g Trans Fat, 43 mg Chol, 937 mg Sod, 32 g Carb, 3 g Fib, 23 g Prot, 103 mg Calc. *POINTS* value: **5.**

BAYOU CHICKEN-AND-SAUSAGE GUMBO

PREP 15 MIN • **COOK** 25 MIN • **SERVES** 4

2   teaspoons canola oil
4   ounces turkey kielbasa, diced
1   onion, chopped
3   celery stalks, chopped
1   green bell pepper, chopped
4   garlic cloves, minced
2   tablespoons all-purpose flour

2   cups reduced-sodium chicken broth
1   cup chopped cooked chicken breast
1   (14 1/2-ounce) can diced tomatoes with green pepper, celery, and onions
1   cup frozen sliced okra
1/4 teaspoon salt
2   cups hot cooked brown rice

1 Heat the oil in a large saucepan over medium-high heat. Add the kielbasa, onion, celery, bell pepper, and garlic; cook, stirring often, until the vegetables are softened, 5 minutes. Add the flour and cook, stirring constantly, 1 minute.

In the Kitchen
Okra is the key ingredient for authentic gumbo, but if it is not to your liking, omit it and add another bell pepper to this recipe.

2 Stir in the broth, chicken, tomatoes, and okra and bring to a boil. Reduce the heat and simmer, uncovered, until slightly thickened, about 15 minutes. Remove from the heat and stir in the salt. Divide the gumbo among 4 bowls and top each with 1/2 cup of the rice.

PER SERVING (1 1/4 cups gumbo with 1/2 cup rice): 307 Cal, 8 g Fat, 2 g Sat Fat, 0 g Trans Fat, 43 mg Chol, 970 mg Sod, 39 g Carb, 7 g Fib, 22 g Prot, 131 mg Calc. *POINTS* value: *6.*

SPICY SHRIMP AND RICE

1 cup long-grain white rice	1½ cups strained tomatoes
1 medium onion, chopped	1 teaspoon Cajun seasoning
1 green bell pepper, chopped	¼ teaspoon red pepper flakes
1 red bell pepper, chopped	¾ pound medium shrimp, peeled and deveined
6 garlic cloves, chopped	1 teaspoon grated lemon zest

1 Cook the rice according to the package directions, omitting the salt if desired; keep warm.

2 Meanwhile, spray a large nonstick skillet with olive oil nonstick spray and set over medium-high heat. Add the onion and peppers and cook, stirring often, until softened, 5 minutes. Add the garlic and cook, stirring, until fragrant, about 30 seconds.

3 Add the tomatoes, seasoning, and pepper flakes and bring to a boil. Reduce the heat and simmer, stirring occasionally, until thickened, about 5 minutes. Stir in the shrimp and simmer until just opaque in the center, about 5 minutes longer. Stir in the lemon zest. Serve with the rice.

In the Kitchen
If you can't find strained tomatoes, use regular canned tomato puree.

PER SERVING (1½ cups shrimp mixture with ¾ cup rice): 252 Cal, 1 g Fat, 0 g Sat Fat, 0 g Trans Fat, 80 mg Chol, 902 mg Sod, 48 g Carb, 4 g Fib, 13 g Prot, 73 mg Calc. **POINTS** value: **4.**

CREAMY CLAM, COD, AND CORN CHOWDER

PREP 15 MIN • **COOK** 25 MIN • **SERVES** 4

4   strips turkey bacon, chopped
2   stalks celery, chopped
4   scallions, thinly sliced
8   ounces red potatoes, scrubbed and cut into $1/2$-inch pieces
2   cups fresh or frozen corn kernels
4   (8-ounce) bottles clam juice

$1/2$ pound manila or other small clams
1   (8-ounce) halibut or cod fillet, cut into 1-inch pieces
1   cup fat-free milk
Pinch black pepper
Pinch cayenne

1 Spray a large saucepan with nonstick spray and set over medium-high heat. Add the bacon, celery, and scallions (reserving a few dark green parts for garnish, if desired) and cook, stirring often, until the celery begins to soften, 3 minutes. Add the potatoes, corn, and clam juice and bring to a boil. Reduce the heat, cover, and simmer until the potatoes are tender, about 10 minutes.

2 Add the clams, cover, and cook until the shells open, 3–5 minutes. Discard any clams that do not open. Reduce the heat to medium-low; stir in the cod and milk and cook until the cod is just opaque in the center, about 2 minutes longer (do not boil). Stir in the pepper and cayenne. Divide the chowder among 4 bowls and sprinkle with the reserved scallion (if using).

▶ Filling Extra
To give this chowder more color and bulk, add 2 medium carrots, peeled and chopped, when you add the potatoes in step 1.

PER SERVING (2 cups): 248 Cal, 5 g Fat, 1 g Sat Fat, 0 g Trans Fat, 55 mg Chol, 935 mg Sod, 30 g Carb, 4 g Fib, 22 g Prot, 154 mg Calc. **POINTS** value: **5.**

CREAMY CLAM, COD, AND CORN CHOWDER

CLASSIC SAN FRANCISCO–STYLE CIOPPINO

PREP 15 MIN • **COOK** 30 MIN • **SERVES** 4

2 teaspoons extra-virgin olive oil
1 large onion, chopped
1 fennel bulb, chopped (fronds reserved)
4 garlic cloves, chopped
$^1/_4$ cup dry red wine
2 (8-ounce) bottles clam juice
1 (28-ounce) can diced tomatoes
1 tablespoon tomato paste

$^1/_2$ teaspoon salt
$^1/_2$ teaspoon black pepper
Pinch cayenne
$^1/_2$ pound manila or other small clams, scrubbed
$^1/_2$ pound mussels, scrubbed and debearded
1 (8-ounce) halibut or cod fillet, cut into 1-inch pieces
$^1/_4$ cup chopped fresh parsley

1 Heat the oil in a large saucepan over medium-high heat. Add the onion, fennel, and garlic; cook, stirring frequently, until the vegetables are softened, 5 minutes. Stir in the wine and cook, stirring occasionally, until almost all the liquid is evaporated, 5 minutes. Stir in the clam juice, tomatoes, tomato paste, salt, pepper, and cayenne and bring to a boil. Reduce the heat, cover, and simmer 10 minutes.

2 Add the clams and cook just until the shells start to open, about 3 minutes. Add the mussels and halibut and cook until the shells of the clams and mussels open and the halibut is opaque in the center, 5 minutes longer. Discard any clams and mussels that do not open. Chop enough of the reserved fennel fronds to equal 2 tablespoons. Stir in the fennel fronds and parsley.

In the Kitchen
You may replace the clams and mussels in this recipe with 8 ounces of halibut or cod.

PER SERVING (2 cups): 176 Cal, 4 g Fat, 1 g Sat Fat, 0 g Trans Fat, 43 mg Chol, 991 mg Sod, 19 g Carb, 5 g Fib, 18 g Prot, 150 mg Calc. **POINTS** value: **3.**

THAI COCONUT CURRY VEGETABLES AND TOFU

PREP 15 MIN • **COOK** 30 MIN • **SERVES** 4

1 medium onion, thinly sliced

1 garlic clove, minced

1 tablespoon minced peeled fresh ginger

2 tablespoons curry powder

$^1/_2$ teaspoon salt

$^1/_4$ teaspoon ground cumin

$^1/_4$ teaspoon ground cardamom

$^1/_2$ cup jasmine rice

1$^1/_2$ cups low-sodium vegetable broth

1 tablespoon low-sodium soy sauce

1 tablespoon honey

3 cups thawed frozen vegetable blend (such as broccoli, carrots, and snow peas)

1 (14-ounce) container extra-firm tofu, drained and cut into $^1/_4$-inch cubes

$^1/_2$ cup reduced-fat coconut milk

$^1/_4$ cup chopped fresh cilantro

1 Spray a large nonstick skillet with nonstick spray, and set over medium-high heat. Add the onion and cook, stirring frequently, until softened, 5 minutes. Add the garlic, ginger, curry powder, salt, cumin, and cardamom and cook, stirring constantly, 1 minute longer. Stir in the rice. Add the broth, soy sauce, and honey and bring to a boil.

> ◗ **Filling Extra**
> Add more nutrients and bulk to this meal by stirring in 2 more cups of the vegetable blend.

2 Reduce the heat, cover, and simmer until the rice is tender and the liquid is almost absorbed, 15 minutes. Stir in the vegetables and tofu and cook, covered, until heated through, 5 minutes. Stir in the coconut milk and cilantro.

PER SERVING (1 cup): 271 Cal, 8 g Fat, 2 g Sat Fat, 0 g Trans Fat, 0 mg Chol, 515 mg Sod, 38 g Carb, 5 g Fib, 15 g Prot, 229 mg Calc. *POINTS* value: **5.**

EASY SKILLET
DINNERS

Chapter 5

SMOTHERED PORK CHOPS WITH ONION GRAVY

PREP 15 MIN • COOK 25 MIN • SERVES 4

4   (6-ounce) bone-in pork loin chops, trimmed
1/2   teaspoon salt
1/4   teaspoon black pepper
1   teaspoon olive oil
2   sweet onions, thinly sliced

1/4   cup water
2   teaspoons all-purpose flour
1   cup reduced-sodium beef broth
1   teaspoon whole-grain Dijon mustard
1   tablespoon chopped fresh thyme

1 Sprinkle the chops with the salt and pepper. Heat the oil in a large nonstick skillet over medium-high heat. Add the chops and cook, turning occasionally, until browned, about 5 minutes. Transfer to a plate.

2 Add the onions and water to the skillet; bring to a boil. Reduce the heat and simmer, covered, stirring occasionally, until the onions are very tender, 12–15 minutes.

3 Sprinkle the onions with the flour; cook, stirring constantly, 1 minute. Add the broth, mustard, and thyme; bring to a boil, stirring until the sauce bubbles and thickens. Return the chops and any accumulated juices to the skillet. Reduce the heat and simmer, uncovered, until the chops are heated through, 2–3 minutes.

> **Filling Extra**
> Serve these hearty chops with steamed kale tossed with lemon zest and crushed red pepper.

PER SERVING (1 chop with 1/4 cup sauce): 253 Cal, 11 g Fat, 4 g Sat Fat, 0 g Trans Fat, 76 mg Chol, 420 mg Sod, 9 g Carb, 2 g Fib, 29 g Prot, 30 mg Calc. **POINTS** value: **6.**

SMOTHERED PORK CHOPS
WITH ONION GRAVY

FETTUCCINE WITH FIRE-ROASTED BOLOGNESE SAUCE

PREP 15 MIN • COOK 1 HR • SERVES 4

2   teaspoons olive oil
$1/4$ pound fresh shiitake mushrooms, stems removed and caps sliced
1   leek, cleaned and thinly sliced (white and light green parts only)
3   garlic cloves, minced
$3/4$ pound lean ground beef (5% fat or less)
1   (28-ounce) can whole fire-roasted tomatoes, drained and chopped

$1/2$ cup dry white wine or reduced-sodium chicken broth
$3/4$ teaspoon salt
8   ounces whole-wheat fettuccine
$1/4$ cup chopped fresh basil
3   tablespoons grated Parmesan

1 To make the sauce, heat the oil in a large skillet over medium heat. Add the mushrooms, leek, and garlic and cook, stirring occasionally, until the vegetables are softened, 6 minutes. Add the beef and cook, breaking it apart with a wooden spoon, until browned, 5 minutes. Add the tomatoes, wine, and salt and bring to a boil. Reduce the heat, cover, and simmer, until the sauce is thickened, about 45 minutes.

In the Kitchen
You can make this recipe using any type or mixture of mushrooms. Look for mixed variety packages of fresh mushrooms in larger supermarkets.

2 Meanwhile, cook the fettuccine according to package directions, omitting the salt if desired. Drain and transfer to a large bowl. Add the sauce, basil, and Parmesan and toss to coat.

PER SERVING (1 cup): 411 Cal, 9 g Fat, 3 g Sat Fat, 0 g Trans Fat, 48 mg Chol, 930 mg Sod, 56 g Carb, 8 g Fib, 30 g Prot, 174 mg Calc. **POINTS** value: **8.**

HOME-STYLE SALISBURY STEAKS WITH MUSHROOM GRAVY

PREP 15 MIN • BROIL/COOK 15 MIN • SERVES 4

1 pound lean ground beef (5% fat or less)

1 onion, finely chopped

2 slices thin-sliced whole-wheat bread, cut into cubes

½ teaspoon salt

⅛ teaspoon black pepper

2 teaspoons olive oil

¼ pound fresh shiitake mushrooms, stems removed and caps sliced

1 tablespoon all-purpose flour

1 cup reduced-sodium beef broth

1 Preheat the broiler. Spray a broiler rack with nonstick spray.

2 Stir the beef, onion, bread, salt, and pepper together in a large bowl until well mixed. Shape into four oval patties. Place the patties on the broiler rack and broil, 6 inches from the heat, until an instant-read thermometer inserted into the side of each patty registers 160°F, about 6 minutes each side.

3 Meanwhile, to make the gravy, heat the oil in a large nonstick skillet over medium-high heat. Add the mushrooms and cook, stirring occasionally, until tender, about 8 minutes. Sprinkle the mushrooms with the flour, stirring to coat. Add the broth and bring to a boil, stirring until the sauce bubbles and thickens. Add the patties to the skillet; reduce the heat, and simmer, uncovered, 2–3 minutes.

> ◗ **Filling Extra**
> Serve this homey entrée with brown rice to soak up the flavorful gravy. A ½ cup cooked brown rice per serving will increase the *POINTS* value by **2.**

PER SERVING (1 patty with ¼ cup gravy): 229 Cal, 8 g Fat, 3 g Sat Fat, 0 g Trans Fat, 59 mg Chol, 442 mg Sod, 11 g Carb, 2 g Fib, 26 g Prot, 29 mg Calc. *POINTS* value: **5.**

SMOKY BBQ PORK
QUESADILLAS WITH
FRESH TOMATO SALSA

SMOKY BBQ PORK QUESADILLAS WITH FRESH TOMATO SALSA

PREP 20 MIN • **COOK** 15 MIN • **SERVES** 4

2   medium tomatoes, chopped

4   tablespoons chopped fresh cilantro

2   tablespoons lime juice

1   garlic clove, minced

2   teaspoons olive oil

1/4   teaspoon salt

3/4   pound pork tenderloin, trimmed and cut into thin strips

1/2   cup barbecue sauce

1   tablespoon chopped pickled jalapeño slices

1/2   cup shredded reduced-fat Monterey Jack

4   (8-inch) multigrain tortillas

1 To make the salsa, stir the tomatoes, 2 tablespoons of the cilantro, lime juice, garlic, oil, and salt together in a medium bowl.

2 Spray a large nonstick skillet with nonstick spray and set over medium-high heat. Add the pork and cook until browned, 5 minutes. Add the barbecue sauce and jalapeños; bring to a boil. Remove from the heat and transfer to a medium bowl. Wipe the skillet clean.

3 Sprinkle 1/4 cup of the cheese on 2 of the tortillas, then top evenly with all of the pork mixture. Sprinkle with the remaining 1/4 cup cheese and remaining 2 tablespoons cilantro. Top with the remaining 2 tortillas, lightly pressing down on each stack.

4 Spray the skillet with nonstick spray and set over medium heat. Add one of the tortilla stacks and cook until lightly browned and heated through, 2–3 minutes on each side. Transfer the quesadilla to a cutting board and keep warm. Repeat with the remaining tortilla stack. Cut each quesadilla into 4 wedges and serve with the salsa.

PER SERVING (2 wedges with 1/2 cup salsa): 341 Cal, 11 g Fat, 4 g Sat Fat, 0 g Trans Fat, 46 mg Chol, 875 mg Sod, 37 g Carb, 3 g Fib, 24 g Prot, 170 mg Calc. **POINTS** value: **7.**

SAUCY CHICKEN MARSALA

PREP 10 MIN • COOK 15 MIN • SERVES 4

4   (5-ounce) skinless, boneless chicken breasts
1/2 teaspoon salt
1/8 teaspoon black pepper
2   teaspoons olive oil
12 ounces sliced mushrooms

1   large shallot, finely chopped
2   garlic cloves, minced
1/2 cup dry Marsala wine
1/2 cup reduced-sodium chicken broth
2   teaspoons chopped fresh thyme

1 Sprinkle the chicken with 1/4 teaspoon of the salt and pepper. Heat 1 teaspoon of the oil in a large nonstick skillet over medium-high heat. Add the chicken and cook until browned and cooked through, 3–4 minutes on each side. Transfer to a plate.

2 Heat the remaining 1 teaspoon oil in the skillet. Add the mushrooms and remaining 1/4 teaspoon salt; cook, stirring occasionally, until the mushrooms are slightly browned, 3–4 minutes. Add the shallot and garlic and cook, stirring often, until the shallots begin to soften, 2 minutes.

▸ **Filling Extra**
Serve this classic Italian dish with a side of whole-wheat linguine (3/4 cup cooked whole-wheat pasta for each serving will increase the *POINTS* value by **2**).

3 Add the Marsala and broth and cook until the sauce thickens slightly, about 1 minute. Return the chicken to the skillet and cook until heated through, 2 minutes. Remove from the heat and stir in the thyme.

PER SERVING (1 chicken breast with about 1/2 cup mushroom mixture): 248 Cal, 7 g Fat, 2 g Sat Fat, 0 g Trans Fat, 88 mg Chol, 452 mg Sod, 8 g Carb, 1 g Fib, 35 g Prot, 32 mg Calc. *POINTS* value: **5.**

CHEESY CHICKEN CARBONARA WITH FETTUCCINE

PREP 10 MIN • **COOK** 20 MIN • **SERVES** 4

6   ounces fettuccine
$^3/_4$ cup fat-free milk
$^1/_3$ cup grated Parmesan
1   large egg, lightly beaten
$^1/_4$ teaspoon salt

$^1/_8$ teaspoon black pepper
4   slices center-cut bacon, chopped
1   small onion, chopped
1   garlic clove, minced
1   cup chopped cooked chicken breast

1 Cook the pasta according to package directions, omitting the salt if desired. Drain and keep warm.

2 Meanwhile, whisk the milk, Parmesan, egg, salt, and pepper in a bowl until blended.

3 Cook the bacon in a large nonstick skillet over medium-high heat, stirring occasionally, until the bacon begins to brown, 3–4 minutes. Add the onion and garlic and cook, stirring often, until the onion begins to brown, 2–3 minutes.

◗ Filling Extra
Add 1 thinly sliced red bell pepper with the onion in step 3.

4 Add the chicken and cook until heated through, 1–2 minutes. Reduce the heat to medium-low, add the fettuccine and the milk mixture. Cook, tossing, until the sauce is thickened and creamy, 2–3 minutes.

PER SERVING (1 cup): 311 Cal, 9 g Fat, 3 g Sat Fat, 0 g Trans Fat, 126 mg Chol, 733 mg Sod, 33 g Carb, 2 g Fib, 24 g Prot, 199 mg Calc. **POINTS** value: **7.**

CHICKEN PAD THAI

PREP 15 MIN • **COOK** 15 MIN • **SERVES** 4

6   ounces rice noodles

1/3 cup ketchup

1   tablespoon sugar

1   tablespoon Asian fish sauce

1/2 teaspoon chili-garlic sauce

2   teaspoons Asian (dark) sesame oil

1   large egg, lightly beaten

1   cup shredded cooked chicken breast

4   scallions, cut into 1/2-inch pieces

2   garlic cloves, minced

2   tablespoons finely chopped unsalted peanuts

1 Cook the noodles according to package directions, omitting the salt if desired; drain. Rinse under cold running water and drain.

2 Meanwhile, stir the ketchup, sugar, fish sauce, and chili-garlic sauce together in a small bowl until blended.

3 Heat 1 teaspoon of the oil in a large nonstick skillet over medium-high heat. Add the egg and cook, stirring occasionally, until set, 2 minutes; transfer to a bowl.

4 Heat the remaining 1 teaspoon oil in the skillet. Add the chicken, scallions, and garlic and cook, stirring occasionally, until the scallions begin to soften, 2–3 minutes. Add the noodles and cook until heated through, 1–2 minutes. Stir in the ketchup mixture and the egg and cook, tossing, until heated through, 1 minute. Divide among 4 plates and sprinkle evenly with the peanuts.

In the Kitchen
Fish sauce is the Thai seasoning equivalent of Chinese soy sauce. It is made from fermented fish, and just a small amount adds a pungent flavor to a dish.

PER SERVING (1 1/4 cups): 324 Cal, 8 g Fat, 2 g Sat Fat, 0 g Trans Fat, 82 mg Chol, 834 mg Sod, 47 g Carb, 2 g Fib, 15 g Prot, 39 mg Calc. *POINTS* value: *7.*

CHICKEN
PAD THAI

Sweet-and-Sour Glazed Chicken

PREP 15 MIN • COOK 10 MIN • SERVES 4

1 pound skinless, boneless chicken breasts, cut into ¹/₂-inch cubes

4 teaspoons cornstarch

4 teaspoons low-sodium soy sauce

¹/₄ cup ketchup

3 tablespoons honey

2 tablespoons rice vinegar

2 teaspoons Asian (dark) sesame oil

2 teaspoons grated peeled fresh ginger

1 green bell pepper, cut into ¹/₂-inch pieces

1 onion, chopped

1 (8-ounce) can pineapple chunks in juice, drained and juice reserved

1 Combine the chicken, 2 teaspoons of the cornstarch, and 2 teaspoons of the soy sauce in a medium bowl; toss to coat. Stir the ketchup, honey, vinegar, reserved pineapple juice, and remaining 2 teaspoons cornstarch and 2 teaspoons soy sauce together in another medium bowl until blended.

2 Heat 1 teaspoon of the oil in a large nonstick skillet over medium-high heat. Add the chicken mixture and cook, stirring often, until the chicken is lightly browned, 4–5 minutes. Transfer to a plate.

▶ **Filling Extra**

The nutty flavor of brown basmati rice is an excellent complement to this saucy dish (¹/₂ cup per serving will increase the **POINTS** value by **2**).

3 Heat the remaining 1 teaspoon oil in the skillet; add the ginger; cook, stirring constantly, until fragrant, 30 seconds. Add the bell pepper and onion and cook, stirring often, until the vegetables begin to soften, 2–3 minutes. Stir in the chicken and pineapple and cook 2 minutes longer. Stir in the ketchup mixture, and cook, stirring constantly, until the mixture comes to a boil and thickens, 1–2 minutes.

PER SERVING (1 cup): 294 Cal, 6 g Fat, 1 g Sat Fat, 0 g Trans Fat, 70 mg Chol, 412 mg Sod, 33 g Carb, 2 g Fib, 27 g Prot, 35 mg Calc. **POINTS** value: **6.**

CHICKEN-AND-SAUSAGE PAELLA

PREP 15 MIN • **COOK** 35 MIN • **SERVES** 6

2   teaspoons olive oil

4   ($\frac{1}{4}$-pound) skinless chicken thighs, trimmed

4   ounces turkey kielbasa, cut into $\frac{1}{4}$-inch slices

1   onion, chopped

1   green bell pepper, chopped

4   garlic cloves, minced

$1\frac{1}{2}$ cups reduced-sodium chicken broth

1   ($14\frac{1}{2}$-ounce) can petite diced tomatoes, drained

$\frac{3}{4}$ cup long-grain white rice

$\frac{1}{2}$ cup frozen peas

8   small pimiento-stuffed olives, sliced

$\frac{1}{2}$ teaspoon saffron threads, crushed

1 Heat the oil in a large nonstick skillet over medium-high heat. Add the chicken and cook until browned, 3–4 minutes on each side. Transfer to a plate.

2 Add the kielbasa to the skillet and cook 1 minute, stirring often, until browned; transfer to the plate with the chicken. Add the onion, bell pepper, and garlic to the skillet; cook, stirring occasionally, until the vegetables begin to soften, 2–3 minutes. Add the chicken, kielbasa, broth, tomatoes, rice, peas, olives, and saffron and bring to a boil. Reduce the heat, cover, and simmer until the rice is tender and the liquid is absorbed, 20 minutes. Remove from the heat and let stand 10 minutes before serving.

PER SERVING (generous $\frac{3}{4}$ cup): 299 Cal, 10 g Fat, 3 g Sat Fat, 0 g Trans Fat, 56 mg Chol, 547 mg Sod, 28 g Carb, 2 g Fib, 23 g Prot, 67 mg Calc. ***POINTS*** value: **6.**

PULLED CHICKEN
SANDWICHES

PULLED CHICKEN SANDWICHES

¹/₂ **cup ketchup**

2 **tablespoons packed dark brown sugar**

1 **tablespoon yellow mustard**

1 **tablespoon apple-cider vinegar**

1 **teaspoon chili powder**

¹/₂ **teaspoon ground cumin**

¹/₈ **teaspoon ground allspice**

¹/₈ **teaspoon ground ginger**

4 **(¹/₄-pound) skinless, boneless chicken thighs, trimmed and cut into 1-inch pieces**

8 **slices whole-wheat bread, toasted**

12 **bread and butter pickle slices**

1 Stir the ketchup, sugar, mustard, vinegar, chili powder, cumin, allspice, and ginger together in a medium skillet; add the chicken and bring to a boil. Reduce the heat, cover, and simmer, stirring occasionally, until the chicken is tender, 20–25 minutes.

2 Remove from the heat and shred the chicken with 2 forks. Serve the chicken mixture between the bread slices with the pickles on the side.

In the Kitchen
Top the sandwiches with thinly sliced red or green cabbage tossed with a little fat-free ranch dressing.

PER SERVING (1 sandwich): 352 Cal, 11 g Fat, 3 g Sat Fat, 0 g Trans Fat, 70 mg Chol, 722 mg Sod, 35 g Carb, 3 g Fib, 29 g Prot, 96 mg Calc. **POINTS** value: **7.**

FAMILY-STYLE SPAGHETTI AND CHICKEN MEATBALLS

PREP 20 MIN • **COOK** 35 MIN • **SERVES** 6

1 pound ground chicken breast	1 medium onion, chopped
2 large eggs	2 garlic cloves, minced
1/2 cup seasoned dried bread crumbs	1 teaspoon dried basil
1/2 cup grated Parmesan	1 (28-ounce) can diced tomatoes
1/4 teaspoon salt	3 tablespoons tomato paste
3 teaspoons olive oil	6 ounces whole-wheat spaghetti

1 To make the meatballs, mix together the chicken, eggs, bread crumbs, Parmesan, and salt in a large bowl. With lightly moistened hands, form the mixture into 18 (1½-inch) meatballs.

2 Heat 2 teaspoons of the oil in a large nonstick skillet over medium-high heat. Add the meatballs and cook, turning occasionally, until browned, 6–8 minutes. Transfer to a plate.

3 Add the remaining 1 teaspoon oil to the skillet. Add the onion, garlic, and basil; cook, stirring occasionally, until the onion begins to soften, 2–3 minutes. Stir in the tomatoes and tomato paste; bring to a boil. Reduce the heat and simmer, uncovered, until the sauce thickens slightly, 10 minutes.

▶ **Filling Extra**
Make a salad with 6 cups baby spinach and 1 cup sliced mushrooms tossed with red-wine vinegar and salt and pepper to taste.

4 Add the meatballs, cover, and simmer until the meatballs are cooked through, 8–10 minutes longer.

5 Meanwhile, cook the spaghetti according to package directions, omitting the salt if desired. Divide the spaghetti among 6 bowls; top evenly with the meatballs and sauce.

PER SERVING (½ cup sauce, ½ cup pasta, and 3 meatballs): 351 Cal, 10 g Fat, 3 g Sat Fat, 0 g Trans Fat, 124 mg Chol, 730 mg Sod, 37 g Carb, 5 g Fib, 30 g Prot, 216 mg Calc. ***POINTS*** value: ***7.***

SALMON CAKES WITH RED PEPPER CHUTNEY

PREP 20 MIN • **COOK** 15 MIN • **SERVES** 4

2 red bell peppers, diced
2 tablespoons red-wine vinegar
1 tablespoon packed light brown sugar
$1/2$ teaspoon whole mustard seeds
1 teaspoon salt
$1/4$ teaspoon red pepper flakes
$1/2$ cup packed flat-leaf parsley leaves

2 tablespoons chopped red onion
1 pound salmon fillets, skinned and cut into 1-inch pieces
1 large egg white
$1/4$ teaspoon black pepper
$1/2$ cup panko bread crumbs
1 bunch watercress, trimmed

1 Bring the bell peppers, vinegar, brown sugar, mustard seeds, $1/2$ teaspoon of the salt, and the pepper flakes to a boil in a small saucepan. Reduce the heat; cover and simmer until the bell peppers are softened, about 10 minutes. Transfer the chutney to a bowl and let cool.

▸ **Filling Extra**
Brown rice would make a lovely accompaniment to this dish ($1/2$ cup cooked rice for each serving will increase the *POINTS* value by **2**).

2 Meanwhile, put the parsley and red onion in a food processor and pulse until coarsely chopped. Add the salmon, egg white, remaining $1/2$ teaspoon salt, and pepper and pulse until the mixture just holds together. Form the salmon mixture into 4 (1-inch-thick) patties. Spread the bread crumbs on a piece of wax paper. Coat the salmon cakes on all sides with the bread crumbs, pressing to adhere.

3 Spray a large nonstick skillet with olive oil nonstick spray and set over medium-high heat. Add the patties and cook until browned and cooked through, 3–4 minutes on each side. Divide the watercress among 4 plates; top with the salmon cakes and serve with the chutney.

PER SERVING (1 salmon cake with $1/2$ cup chutney and 1 cup watercress): 235 Cal, 7 g Fat, 2 g Sat Fat, 0 g Trans Fat, 74 mg Chol, 738 mg Sod, 14 g Carb, 2 g Fib, 27 g Prot, 71 mg Calc. *POINTS* value: **5**.

SEAFOOD LINGUINE WITH TOMATOES AND LEMON

PREP 15 MIN • **COOK** 20 MIN • **SERVES** 4

8   ounces whole-wheat linguine
2   large tomatoes, chopped
1/4 cup thinly sliced scallions
2   teaspoons grated lemon zest
1/4 cup lemon juice
1   garlic clove, minced

3/4 teaspoon salt
1/4 teaspoon black pepper
3   teaspoons olive oil
1   (8-ounce) skinless salmon fillet
8   ounces peeled and deveined medium shrimp
1/4 cup chopped flat-leaf parsley

1 Cook the pasta according to package directions, omitting the salt if desired; drain and keep warm.

2 Meanwhile, combine the tomatoes, scallions, lemon zest, lemon juice, garlic, 1/2 teaspoon of the salt, and 1/8 teaspoon of the pepper in a large bowl.

3 Heat 1/2 teaspoon of the oil in a large nonstick skillet over medium-high heat. Sprinkle the salmon and shrimp with the remaining 1/4 teaspoon salt and 1/8 teaspoon pepper. Add the salmon and cook until just opaque in the center, about 3 minutes on each side. Transfer to a plate. Wipe the skillet clean. Add 1/2 teaspoon of the remaining oil to the skillet; add the shrimp and cook, stirring often, until the shrimp are just opaque in the center, 3–4 minutes.

In the Kitchen
You can substitute 2 cups halved cherry or grape tomatoes for the chopped tomatoes. This recipe works with the **Simply Filling technique.**

4 Break the salmon into small pieces with 2 forks; add to the tomato mixture. Add the pasta, shrimp, parsley, and remaining 2 teaspoons olive oil; toss to combine.

PER SERVING (2 cups): 380 Cal, 8 g Fat, 2 g Sat Fat, 0 g Trans Fat, 118 mg Chol, 790 mg Sod, 49 g Carb, 6 g Fib, 31 g Prot, 71 mg Calc. *POINTS* value: *7.*

SCALLOPS WITH CORN-AND-TOMATO SALAD

PREP 15 MIN • **COOK** 15 MIN • **SERVES** 4

3   ears corn-on-the-cob, kernels removed
3   medium tomatoes, seeded and chopped
2   scallions, thinly sliced
¼   cup chopped fresh parsley
2   tablespoons white-wine vinegar

1½ teaspoons extra-virgin olive oil
1   teaspoon salt
½   teaspoon black pepper
1   pound sea scallops
½   teaspoon ground coriander

1 To make the salad, bring a medium saucepan of water to a boil. Add the corn and cook until crisp-tender, 3 minutes. Drain in a colander and transfer to a large bowl. Add the tomatoes, scallions, parsley, vinegar, oil, ½ teaspoon of the salt, and ¼ teaspoon of the pepper.

2 Spray a large heavy skillet with olive oil nonstick spray and set over medium-high heat. Pat the scallops dry with paper towels. Sprinkle with the coriander and remaining ½ teaspoon salt and ¼ teaspoon pepper. Add the scallops and cook just until browned and opaque in the center, 2–3 minutes on each side. Serve with the corn salad.

> **◆ Filling Extra**
> Add 1 cup peeled and chopped cucumber to the corn salad. This recipe works with the **Simply Filling technique.**

PER SERVING (5 scallops with 1 cup corn salad): 185 Cal, 4 g Fat, 1 g Sat Fat, 0 g Trans Fat, 30 mg Chol, 749 mg Sod, 24 g Carb, 5 g Fib, 17 g Prot, 92 mg Calc. **POINTS** value: **3.**

SKILLET MACARONI AND CHEESE

PREP 10 MIN • **COOK/BROIL** 15 MIN • **SERVES** 4

8 ounces whole-wheat macaroni
1 tablespoon butter
1 tablespoon + 2 teaspoons all-purpose flour
1 1/2 cups fat-free milk
1 cup shredded reduced-fat sharp cheddar

1/2 teaspoon salt
1/8 teaspoon black pepper
1 tablespoon plain dried bread crumbs
1 tablespoon grated Parmesan

1 Cook the macaroni according to package directions, omitting the salt if desired; drain.

2 Meanwhile, melt the butter in a large ovenproof skillet over medium heat. Add the flour and cook, whisking constantly, for 1 minute. Gradually whisk in the milk. Increase the heat and cook, whisking constantly, until the mixture comes to a boil and thickens slightly, about 5 minutes. Remove from the heat and add the cheddar, salt, and pepper, whisking until the cheese is melted. Add the pasta to the cheese sauce, stirring to coat.

In the Kitchen
You can substitute 8 ounces whole-wheat fusilli for the macaroni if you wish.

3 Preheat the broiler.

4 Stir the bread crumbs and Parmesan together in a small bowl; sprinkle over the macaroni and cheese in the skillet. Broil 5 inches from the heat source, until the crumbs are browned, about 1 minute.

PER SERVING (about 1 cup): 324 Cal, 6 g Fat, 4 g Sat Fat, 0 g Trans Fat, 17 mg Chol, 843 mg Sod, 50 g Carb, 5 g Fib, 20 g Prot, 366 mg Calc. **POINTS** value: **6.**

SKILLET MACARONI
AND CHEESE

MUSSELS PUTTANESCA WITH LINGUINE

PREP 15 MIN • **COOK** 20 MIN • **SERVES** 4

8 ounces whole-wheat linguine

1 (28-ounce) can whole tomatoes with their juice

4 garlic cloves, minced

5 kalamata olives, pitted and chopped

2 tablespoons capers, rinsed

1/4 teaspoon salt

1/4 teaspoon black pepper

Pinch red pepper flakes

1 1/2 pounds mussels, scrubbed and debearded

2 tablespoons chopped flat-leaf parsley

1/4 cup grated Parmesan

1 Cook the pasta according to package directions, omitting the salt if desired; drain and keep warm.

2 Meanwhile, place the tomatoes in a food processor and pulse until pureed.

3 Spray a large deep nonstick skillet with olive oil nonstick spray and set over medium-high heat. Add the garlic and cook, stirring, until fragrant, 30 seconds. Stir in the tomatoes, olives, capers, salt, pepper, and pepper flakes and bring to a boil. Reduce the heat and simmer until slightly thickened, about 8 minutes. Add the mussels, cover, and cook until the shells open, about 5 minutes. Discard any mussels that do not open. Add the linguine and parsley and toss to combine. Divide the mixture among 4 bowls and sprinkle evenly with the cheese.

In the Kitchen
You can make this recipe using 1 pound peeled and deveined shrimp instead of the mussels. Cook the shrimp until they are opaque in the center, about 5 minutes.

PER SERVING (9 mussels with scant 1 cup sauce and 1 cup linguine): 391 Cal, 7 g Fat, 2 g Sat Fat, 0 g Trans Fat, 45 mg Chol, 1,128 mg Sod, 56 g Carb, 9 g Fib, 29 g Prot, 190 mg Calc. *POINTS* value: *8.*

CHINESE TOFU WITH MUSHROOMS AND BOK CHOY

PREP 20 MIN • COOK 15 MIN • SERVES 4

1   (14-ounce) container extra-firm tofu
4   teaspoons cornstarch
1/2 cup low-sodium vegetable broth
2   tablespoons low-sodium soy sauce
2   teaspoons honey
2   teaspoons Asian (dark) sesame oil
2   teaspoons canola oil

1   tablespoon minced peeled fresh ginger
4   baby bok choy, quartered lengthwise
8   ounces shiitake mushrooms, stems removed and caps sliced
2   scallions, thinly sliced on a diagonal
1/8 teaspoon crushed red pepper

1 Place the tofu between 2 flat plates. Weight the top plate with a heavy can until the tofu bulges at the sides but does not split, about 30 minutes. Pour off the water that has accumulated on the bottom of the plate. Cut the tofu into $1/2$-inch cubes and pat dry with paper towels. Sprinkle the tofu evenly with 2 teaspoons of the cornstarch.

2 Whisk together the broth, soy sauce, honey, sesame oil, and remaining 2 teaspoons cornstarch in a small bowl. Set aside.

3 Heat 1 teaspoon of the canola oil in a large nonstick skillet over medium-high heat. Add the tofu and cook, stirring occasionally, until lightly browned, about 5 minutes. Transfer to a plate.

4 Add the remaining 1 teaspoon canola oil to the skillet. Add the ginger and cook, stirring constantly, until fragrant, 30 seconds. Add the bok choy, mushrooms, scallions, and crushed red pepper and cook, stirring constantly, until the vegetables are crisp-tender, 5 minutes.

> **Filling Extra**
> Serve this spicy stir-fry with brown rice ($1/2$ cup cooked brown rice per serving will increase the **POINTS** value by **2**).

5 Add the tofu and the broth mixture to the skillet and cook, stirring constantly, until the mixture comes to a boil and thickens, about 1 minute.

PER SERVING (1½ cups): 190 Cal, 11 g Fat, 1 g Sat Fat, 0 g Trans Fat, 0 mg Chol, 421 mg Sod, 14 g Carb, 3 g Fib, 12 g Prot, 228 mg Calc. **POINTS** value: **4**.

VEGGIE-PACKED ANGEL HAIR PASTA WITH PEANUTS

PREP 15 MIN • COOK 15 MIN • SERVES 4

8   ounces whole-wheat capellini

2   teaspoons canola oil

2   tablespoons minced peeled fresh ginger

1   garlic clove, minced

4   cups broccoli florets

1   red bell pepper, chopped

1   medium onion, thinly sliced

$^1/_4$ cup sake or reduced-sodium chicken broth

$^1/_4$ cup hoisin sauce

2   cups thawed frozen shelled edamame (green soybeans)

3   scallions, thinly sliced on a diagonal

2   tablespoons chopped unsalted peanuts

1 Cook the capellini according to the package directions, omitting the salt if desired.

2 Meanwhile, heat the oil in a large nonstick skillet over medium-high heat. Add the ginger and garlic and cook, stirring constantly, until fragrant, 30 seconds. Add the broccoli, bell pepper, and onion, and cook, stirring constantly until the vegetables begin to soften, 2 minutes. Add the sake and cook until almost evaporated, 2 minutes. Stir in the hoisin sauce and cook, stirring constantly, 2 minutes. Add the edamame and scallions and cook until heated through, 2 minutes longer.

◗ Filling Extra
Add 1 cup of thinly sliced carrots or 1 cup of sliced mushrooms—or both—when you add the broccoli in step 2.

3 Divide the capellini among 4 plates; top each serving evenly with the vegetable mixture and sprinkle each serving with $^1/_2$ tablespoon of the peanuts.

PER SERVING (1$^1/_2$ cups): 418 Cal, 10 g Fat, 1 g Sat Fat, 0 g Trans Fat, 0 mg Chol, 492 mg Sod, 69 g Carb, 12 g Fib, 20 g Prot, 124 mg Calc. *POINTS* value: *8.*

GARLICKY FARFALLE WITH WHITE BEANS AND ARUGULA

PREP 10 MIN • **COOK** 20 MIN • **SERVES** 4

2 cups whole-wheat farfalle (bow ties)
1 tablespoon olive oil
6 garlic cloves, thinly sliced
1 (15½-ounce) can cannellini (white kidney) beans, rinsed and drained

2 (5-ounce) bags baby arugula
¼ cup chopped walnuts, toasted
1 tablespoon grated lemon zest
1 tablespoon lemon juice
¼ cup grated Parmesan

1 Cook the farfalle according to the package directions, omitting the salt if desired. Drain, reserving ¼ cup of the cooking liquid, and keep warm.

2 Heat the oil in a large nonstick skillet over medium-high heat. Add the garlic and cook, stirring constantly, just until the garlic begins to brown, about 1 minute. Add the beans and the reserved cooking liquid and cook, stirring often, until the beans are heated through, 3 minutes. Add the arugula, in batches if necessary, and cook, stirring constantly, just until wilted, 2–3 minutes.

> **Filling Extra**
> Add 2 cups halved cherry tomatoes when you add the pasta in step 3.

3 Stir in the pasta, walnuts, lemon zest, and lemon juice. Divide the pasta mixture among 4 plates and sprinkle evenly with the Parmesan.

PER SERVING (1½ cups): 361 Cal, 11 g Fat, 2 g Sat Fat, 0 g Trans Fat, 5 mg Chol, 494 mg Sod, 51 g Carb, 9 g Fib, 18 g Prot, 297 mg Calc. *POINTS* value: **7.**

CREAMY RISOTTO
PRIMAVERA

CREAMY RISOTTO PRIMAVERA

PREP 15 MIN • COOK 35 MIN • SERVES 6

6   cups reduced-sodium vegetable broth
1   tablespoon olive oil
1   medium onion, chopped
2   cups shiitake mushrooms, stems removed and caps sliced
2   garlic cloves, minced
1¹/₂ cups Arborio rice
¹/₃ cup dry white wine or reduced-sodium chicken broth

2   cups thawed frozen baby peas
2   large yellow squash, quartered lengthwise and cut into ¹/₂-inch pieces
1   tablespoon grated lemon zest
¹/₂ cup chopped fresh flat-leaf parsley
¹/₂ cup grated Parmesan
¹/₄ teaspoon black pepper

1 Bring the broth to a boil in a large saucepan; reduce the heat and keep at a simmer.

2 Heat the oil in a large deep-sided skillet over medium-high heat. Add the onion, mushrooms, and garlic and cook, stirring frequently, until softened, 5 minutes. Add the rice and cook, stirring, until the outer shell of the rice grains is translucent, about 1 minute.

3 Add the wine and stir until absorbed. Add the hot broth, ¹/₂ cup at a time, stirring until it is absorbed before adding more, until the rice is just tender. Add the peas, squash, and lemon zest with the last addition of the broth. The cooking time should be 20–25 minutes from the first addition of broth. Stir in the parsley, Parmesan, and pepper.

PER SERVING (1 cup): 326 Cal, 6 g Fat, 2 g Sat Fat, 0 g Trans Fat, 6 mg Chol, 480 mg Sod, 58 g Carb, 4 g Fib, 12 g Prot, 173 mg Calc. **POINTS** value: **6.**

Cozy Meals from THE Oven

Chapter 6

AUTUMN POT ROAST WITH HORSERADISH SAUCE

PREP 15 MIN • COOK/BAKE 2 HRS 30 MIN • SERVES 8

2 pounds boneless bottom round roast, trimmed

$3/4$ teaspoon salt

2 teaspoons olive oil

$1/2$ cup reduced-sodium beef broth

1 onion, chopped

3 garlic cloves, chopped

1 tablespoon chopped fresh thyme

$1^1/4$ pounds baby potatoes, halved

$1^1/2$ cups baby carrots

2 medium turnips, peeled and cut into 1-inch pieces

$1/2$ cup fat-free plain Greek yogurt

3 tablespoons prepared horseradish

1 teaspoon Dijon mustard

1 Preheat the oven to 350°F.

2 Sprinkle the beef with $1/2$ teaspoon of the salt. Heat the oil in a Dutch oven over medium-high heat. Add the beef and cook, turning frequently, until browned, about 8 minutes. Add the broth, stirring to scrape any browned bits from the bottom of the pot. Add the onion, garlic, and thyme; bring to a boil. Cover and bake, turning once, $1^1/2$ hours.

3 Add the potatoes, carrots, and turnips to the Dutch oven. Bake, covered, until the beef and vegetables are fork-tender, 45 minutes.

4 Meanwhile, to make the horseradish sauce, combine the yogurt, horseradish, mustard, and the remaining $1/4$ teaspoon salt in a small bowl. Cover and refrigerate until ready to use.

5 Transfer the beef to a cutting board and slice across the grain into 16 slices. Serve with the vegetables and the horseradish sauce.

In the Kitchen

Substitute cubes of sweet potatoes, butternut squash, or parsnips for the baby potatoes, carrots, or turnips. This recipe works with the **Simply Filling technique.**

PER SERVING (2 slices beef with generous $1/2$ cup vegetables and $1^1/2$ tablespoons horseradish sauce): 287 Cal, 6 g Fat, 2 g Sat Fat, 0 g Trans Fat, 84 mg Chol, 359 mg Sod, 20 g Carb, 3 g Fib, 37 g Prot, 77 mg Calc. **POINT**S value: **6.**

AUTUMN POT ROAST WITH
HORSERADISH SAUCE

Rosemary-Mustard-Crusted Beef Roast

PREP 10 MIN • **BAKE** 1 HR • **SERVES** 8

2 tablespoons seasoned dried bread crumbs

2 tablespoons Dijon mustard

2 teaspoons chopped fresh rosemary

2 teaspoons olive oil

$\frac{1}{2}$ teaspoon salt

$\frac{1}{4}$ teaspoon black pepper

1 (2-pound) boneless eye-round roast, trimmed

1 Preheat the oven to 400°F. Spray a small roasting pan with nonstick spray.

2 Combine the bread crumbs, mustard, rosemary, oil, salt, and pepper in a small bowl. Rub the mixture over the top and sides of the beef. Place in the pan and roast, uncovered, until an instant-read thermometer inserted in the center of the roast registers 145°F for medium-rare, about 1 hour. Transfer to a cutting board and let stand 10 minutes. Cut the roast into 24 slices.

> ◗ **Filling Extra**
> Complete the meal with baked potatoes and steamed broccoli. A 5-ounce baked potato for each serving will increase the **POINTS** value by **2.**

PER SERVING (3 slices): 199 Cal, 6 g Fat, 2 g Sat Fat, 0 g Trans Fat, 81 mg Chol, 294 mg Sod, 2 g Carb, 0 g Fib, 33 g Prot, 11 mg Calc. **POINTS** value: **4.**

BEEF-AND-BEAN CHILES RELLENOS BAKE

PREP 20 MIN • COOK/BAKE 50 MIN • SERVES 4

4   large poblano chiles
2   teaspoons canola oil
1   onion, chopped
2   garlic cloves, minced
$^1/_2$ pound lean ground beef (5% fat or less)
1   teaspoon chili powder

$^1/_2$ teaspoon ground cumin
$^3/_4$ cup canned black beans, rinsed and drained
$^3/_4$ cup cooked brown rice
1   cup fat-free mild green salsa
$^1/_4$ cup shredded fat-free Monterey Jack

1 To roast the peppers, preheat the boiler. Line a baking sheet with foil and place the chiles on the foil. Broil 5 inches from the heat, turning frequently with tongs, until the skins blister, about 10 minutes. Transfer the peppers to a counter and wrap in the foil. Let steam for about 15 minutes. When cool enough to handle, peel the blackened skin off the peppers. Use a sharp knife to make a long slit in one side of each pepper; remove the seeds and membranes, being careful not to tear the peppers.

2 Preheat the oven to 375°F. Spray a 7 x 11-inch baking dish with nonstick spray.

3 Heat the oil in a large nonstick skillet over medium-high heat. Add the onion and garlic; cook, stirring occasionally, until tender, 5 minutes. Add the beef, chili powder, and cumin and cook, breaking up the meat with a spoon, until browned, about 5 minutes. Remove the skillet from the heat and stir in the beans and rice.

4 Gently stuff about $^1/_2$ cup of the filling into each poblano pepper, mounding the filling and taking care not to split the skin. Place the peppers in the baking dish. Top evenly with the salsa and sprinkle with the cheese. Cover loosely with foil and bake 20 minutes. Remove the foil and bake until lightly browned, 10 minutes.

In the Kitchen
Leave behind some tiny bits of the charred skin when you peel roasted peppers to give a smokier flavor. This recipe works with the **Simply Filling technique.**

PER SERVING (1 stuffed pepper): 240 Cal, 6 g Fat, 2 g Sat Fat, 0 g Trans Fat, 31 mg Chol, 541 mg Sod, 29 g Carb, 8 g Fib, 19 g Prot, 117 mg Calc. **POINTS** value: **5.**

CONFETTI MEATLOAF
WITH CAJUN
BARBECUE SAUCE

CONFETTI MEATLOAF WITH CAJUN BARBECUE SAUCE

PREP 10 MIN • **COOK/BAKE** 1 HR 10 MIN • **SERVES** 6

2 slices whole grain sandwich bread, cut into cubes

$^1/_2$ cup fat-free milk

2 teaspoons olive oil

1 onion, chopped

1 green bell pepper, diced

1 red bell pepper, diced

1 pound lean ground beef (5% fat or less)

1 large egg, lightly beaten

$^1/_2$ teaspoon Southwest seasoning

$^1/_4$ cup hot and spicy barbecue sauce

1 Preheat the oven to 350°F. Line a rimmed baking sheet with foil; spray the foil with nonstick spray.

2 Stir the bread and milk together in a large bowl. Let stand 10 minutes.

3 Meanwhile, heat the oil in a large nonstick skillet over medium-high heat. Add the onion and bell peppers and cook, stirring occasionally, until tender, about 8 minutes. Transfer to a plate and let cool slightly.

4 Add the onion mixture, beef, egg, and seasoning to the bread mixture; mix just until blended. Transfer the mixture to the baking sheet and form into a 4 x 9-inch loaf. Spread the barbecue sauce over the top of the loaf. Bake until an instant-read thermometer inserted into the center of the loaf registers 160°F, about 1 hour. Let stand 5 minutes before slicing. Cut into 12 slices.

PER SERVING (2 slices): 187 Cal, 6 g Fat, 2 g Sat Fat, 0 g Trans Fat, 75 mg Chol, 220 mg Sod, 13 g Carb, 2 g Fib, 18 g Prot, 58 mg Calc. **POINTS** value: **4.**

SWEET-AND-SOUR STUFFED CABBAGE

PREP 20 MIN • COOK/BAKE 1 HR 50 MIN • SERVES 4

1   (5¹/₄-ounce) package boil-in-the-bag brown rice
1   medium head Savoy cabbage
¹/₂   pound cremini mushrooms, thinly sliced
1   onion, finely chopped
³/₄   pound lean ground beef (5% fat or less)

1   large egg
¹/₂   teaspoon salt
1   (25-ounce) jar fat-free marinara sauce
2   tablespoons apple-cider vinegar
1   tablespoon packed brown sugar

1 Prepare the rice according to package directions. Transfer to a large bowl and let cool slightly.

2 Meanwhile, bring a large pot of water to a boil. Carefully separate the cabbage leaves, place in the water, and cook just until wilted, 1–2 minutes. Drain and let stand until cool enough to handle. Reserve 8 large leaves. Thinly slice the remaining cabbage.

3 Preheat the oven to 350°F. Spray a 9 x 13-inch baking dish with nonstick spray.

4 To make the filling, spray a large nonstick skillet with nonstick spray and set over medium-high heat. Add the mushrooms and onion and cook, stirring occasionally, until tender, about 8 minutes. Add the mushroom mixture, beef, egg, and salt to the rice; mix well.

In the Kitchen
Lining the bottom of the baking dish with sliced cabbage helps prevent the rolls from sticking to the bottom of the pan.

5 Divide the beef mixture among the cabbage leaves. Fold in the sides of the leaves over the stuffing, then roll the leaves to enclose the filling. Place the sliced cabbage in the prepared baking dish. Arrange the cabbage rolls, seam-side down, on the sliced cabbage.

6 Stir the marinara sauce, vinegar, and brown sugar together in a medium bowl. Pour the sauce over the rolls. Cover and bake, basting occasionally, until the cabbage is tender and an instant-read thermometer inserted into the center of each roll registers 160°F, 1¹/₂–2 hours.

PER SERVING (2 stuffed rolls): 389 Cal, 8 g Fat, 3 g Sat Fat, 0 g Trans Fat, 98 mg Chol, 962 mg Sod, 55 g Carb, 8 g Fib, 28 g Prot, 115 mg Calc. *POINTS* value: *8*.

ROAST PORK WITH GINGERSNAP GRAVY

PREP 15 MIN • BAKE/COOK 1 HR • SERVES 8

2 teaspoons olive oil
1 teaspoon dried thyme
³/₄ teaspoon salt
¹/₄ teaspoon black pepper
1 (2-pound) boneless center-cut pork loin roast, trimmed
1 shallot, finely chopped

1 garlic clove, minced
³/₄ cup reduced-sodium beef broth
4 reduced-fat gingersnap cookies, crushed
1 teaspoon packed brown sugar
1 teaspoon unsalted butter

1 Preheat the oven to 375°F. Spray a shallow roasting pan with nonstick spray.

2 Combine 1 teaspoon of the oil, thyme, ¹/₂ teaspoon of the salt, and pepper in a small bowl. Rub the spice mixture all over the pork. Put the pork in the pan and roast until an instant-read thermometer inserted in the center registers 155°F, 1 hour. Transfer the pork to a cutting board, cover loosely with foil, and let stand 10 minutes (the temperature will increase to 160°F for medium).

3 Meanwhile, to make the sauce, heat the remaining 1 teaspoon oil in a small saucepan over medium heat. Add the shallot and garlic and cook, stirring constantly, until fragrant, 1 minute. Add the broth, gingersnaps, sugar, and the remaining ¹/₄ teaspoon salt; bring to a boil. Boil 1 minute. Remove the pan from the heat and swirl in the butter. Cut the pork into 16 slices and serve with the sauce.

> **Filling Extra**
> Serve the pork with a side of unsweetened applesauce (¹/₂ cup for each serving will increase the **POINTS** value by **1**).

PER SERVING (2 slices pork with ¹/₄ cup sauce): 224 Cal, 11 g Fat, 4 g Sat Fat, 0 g Trans Fat, 73 mg Chol, 303 mg Sod, 4 g Carb, 0 g Fib, 26 g Prot, 14 mg Calc. **POINTS** value: **5.**

BRAISED LAMB SHANKS WITH GREMOLATA

PREP 20 MIN • COOK/BAKE 1 HR 45 MIN • SERVES 4

4 (7-ounce) lamb shanks, trimmed
3/4 teaspoon salt
1/2 teaspoon black pepper
1 onion, chopped
1 carrot, chopped
1 celery stalk, chopped
3 garlic cloves, minced
1 (14 1/2-ounce) can diced tomatoes

1 cup reduced-sodium beef broth
1/4 cup dry white wine
1 tablespoon chopped fresh rosemary
1 (15 1/2-ounce) can cannellini (white kidney) beans, rinsed and drained
1/4 cup chopped fresh parsley
2 tablespoons grated lemon zest

1 Preheat the oven to 350°F.

2 Spray a large nonstick skillet with nonstick spray and set over medium-high heat. Sprinkle the lamb with 1/4 teaspoon of the salt and 1/4 teaspoon of the pepper. Place the lamb in the skillet and cook, turning often, until browned on all sides, 5 minutes. Transfer the lamb to a Dutch oven.

3 Add the onion, carrot, celery, and 2 cloves of the garlic to the skillet. Cook, covered, over medium heat, stirring occasionally, until the vegetables are tender, 8–10 minutes. Add the tomatoes, broth, wine, the remaining 1/2 teaspoon salt, remaining 1/4 teaspoon pepper, and rosemary; bring to a boil, stirring to scrape the browned bits from the bottom of the skillet.

In the Kitchen
If you can't find 7-ounce lamb shanks, use 2 (1-pound) lamb shanks instead and divide the meat into 4 servings after cooking.

4 Pour the vegetable mixture over the lamb. Bake, covered, until the meat is almost tender, about 1 hour. Add the beans and continue to bake, covered, until the meat is fork-tender, about 30 minutes longer.

5 To make the gremolata, stir the parsley, lemon zest, and remaining garlic clove together in a small bowl. Sprinkle over the lamb shanks.

PER SERVING (1 shank with 3/4 cup beans and sauce): 379 Cal, 11 g Fat, 4 g Sat Fat, 0 g Trans Fat, 99 mg Chol, 963 mg Sod, 30 g Carb, 7 g Fib, 40 g Prot, 143 mg Calc. *POINTS* value: **8.**

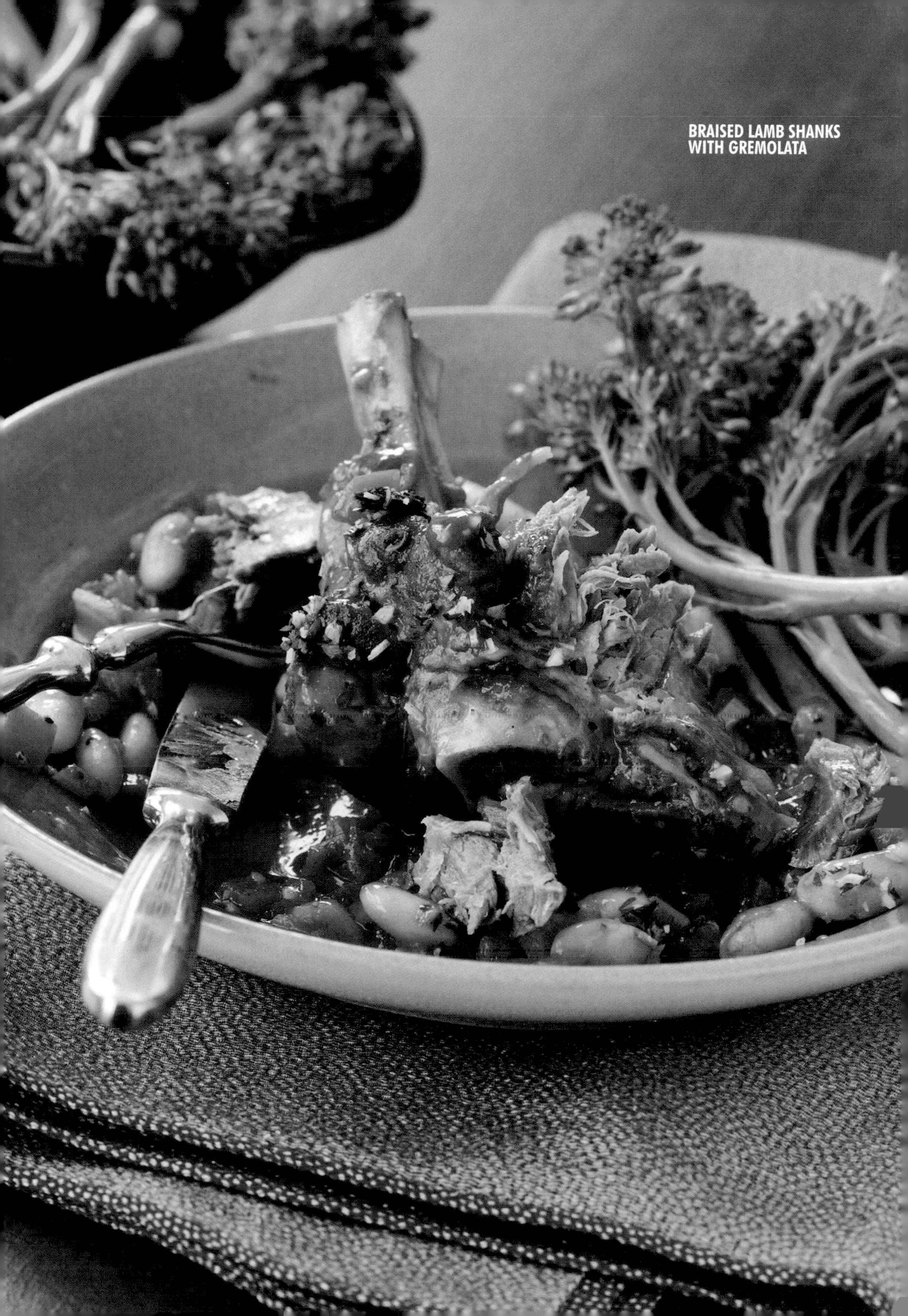

BRAISED LAMB SHANKS
WITH GREMOLATA

ROSEMARY ROASTED CHICKEN

PREP 10 MIN • **ROAST** 1 HR 15 MIN • **SERVES** 6

1   (3½-pound) whole chicken, giblets discarded
1½ tablespoons light butter, softened
1   tablespoon chopped fresh rosemary

2   garlic cloves, minced
¾ teaspoon salt
¼ teaspoon black pepper

1 Preheat the oven to 375°F. Spray a medium roasting pan with nonstick spray.

2 Stir the butter, rosemary, garlic, salt, and pepper together in a small bowl. Loosen the skin from the breasts and legs of the chicken; rub the paste under the skin. Tuck the wings under and tie the legs. Place in the prepared roasting pan, breast side up.

3 Roast the chicken until an instant-read thermometer inserted in a thigh registers 180°F, 1¼–1½ hours. Remove the chicken from the oven and transfer to a carving board. Let stand 10 minutes before carving. Discard the chicken skin before eating.

> **Filling Extra**
> While you roast the chicken, place 1½ pounds baby potatoes in a separate pan and bake 45 minutes. The per-serving **POINTS** value will increase by **1**.

PER SERVING (⅙ of chicken): 191 Cal, 8 g Fat, 3 g Sat Fat, 0 g Trans Fat, 86 mg Chol, 392 mg Sod, 0 g Carb, 0 g Fib, 27 g Prot, 18 mg Calc. **POINTS** value: **4**.

BEER-CAN CHICKEN

PREP 10 MIN • BAKE 1 HR 15 MIN • SERVES 6

2   tablespoons salt-free all-purpose
    seasoning blend
1   tablespoon sugar
³/₄ teaspoon salt

1   (3¹/₂-pound) whole chicken, giblets discarded
1   (12-ounce) can beer

1 Preheat the oven to 375°F. Spray a medium roasting pan with nonstick spray.

2 Stir the seasoning blend, sugar, and salt together in a small bowl. Loosen the skin from the breasts and legs of the chicken; rub the seasoning mixture under and over the skin.

3 Pour off ¹/₄ of the beer. Hold the chicken upright with the opening of the cavity pointing down. Slide the cavity of the chicken over the can. Set the chicken with the can bottom in the prepared roasting pan, standing upright.

4 Roast the chicken until an instant-read thermometer inserted in a thigh registers 180°F, 1¹/₄–1¹/₂ hours. Remove the chicken from the oven and transfer to a carving board. Let stand 10 minutes and carefully remove and discard the beer can before carving. Discard the chicken skin before eating.

In the Kitchen
Cooking chicken with an open can of beer in the cavity creates steam as the chicken cooks, helping keep it moist. It also adds a subtle beer flavor to the chicken.

PER SERVING (¹/₆ of chicken): 189 Cal, 7 g Fat, 2 g Sat Fat, 0 g Trans Fat, 83 mg Chol, 375 mg Sod, 3 g Carb, 0 g Fib, 27 g Prot, 26 mg Calc. **POINTS** value: **4.**

Oven-Barbecued Chicken with Mop Sauce

PREP 15 MIN • COOK 50 MIN • SERVES 6

4   tablespoons packed dark brown sugar
1   tablespoon paprika
1   tablespoon + 1 teaspoon chili powder
2   teaspoons ground cumin
1/4 teaspoon ground allspice
3/4 teaspoon salt

1   (3½-pound) chicken, cut into 6 pieces, skin and wings discarded
1/3 cup ketchup
2   tablespoons apple-cider vinegar
1/2 teaspoon Worcestershire sauce

1 Preheat the oven to 425°F. Line a roasting pan with foil and spray with nonstick spray.

2 Stir 2 tablespoons of the sugar, paprika, 1 tablespoon of the chili powder, cumin, allspice, and salt together in a small bowl. Rub the mixture all over the chicken to coat. Stir the remaining 2 tablespoons sugar, 1 teaspoon chili powder, ketchup, vinegar, and Worcestershire sauce together in a small bowl.

3 Place the chicken in the prepared roasting pan and bake 35 minutes. Remove from the oven, drizzle with the ketchup mixture, and turn to coat. Bake until the chicken is cooked through, 15 minutes longer.

PER SERVING (⅙ of chicken): 228 Cal, 6 g Fat, 2 g Sat Fat, 0 g Trans Fat, 85 mg Chol, 549 mg Sod, 14 g Carb, 1 g Fib, 28 g Prot, 39 mg Calc. **POINTS** value: **5.**

MOM'S CHICKEN-AND-BISCUIT POT PIE

1½ cups reduced-sodium chicken broth
½ cup fat-free half-and-half
2 tablespoons all-purpose flour
1 tablespoon Dijon mustard
¼ teaspoon black pepper
1 tablespoon unsalted butter
1 medium onion, chopped
1 fennel bulb, chopped

3 garlic cloves, minced
¼ teaspoon dried thyme
2 cups frozen mixed vegetables (corn, carrots, peas, and green beans)
1½ cups chopped cooked chicken breast
1 (6-ounce) package refrigerated buttermilk biscuits

1 Preheat the oven to 425°F. Spray a 3-quart shallow baking dish with nonstick spray.

2 Whisk the broth, half-and-half, flour, mustard, and pepper in a medium bowl until blended.

3 Melt the butter in a large nonstick skillet over medium-high heat. Add the onion, fennel, garlic, and thyme and cook, stirring occasionally, until softened, 6 minutes. Stir in the mixed vegetables and chicken and cook until heated through, 3 minutes. Add the broth mixture and cook, stirring constantly, until the mixture comes to a boil and thickens, 2–3 minutes. Pour into the prepared baking dish. Arrange the biscuits on top of the chicken mixture.

4 Bake until the filling is bubbly and the biscuits are golden brown, 10–12 minutes.

PER SERVING (generous 1 cup chicken and vegetables with 1 biscuit): 306 Cal, 10 g Fat, 3 g Sat Fat, 2 g Trans Fat, 42 mg Chol, 757 mg Sod, 35 g Carb, 6 g Fib, 20 g Prot, 105 mg Calc. *POINTS* value: *6.*

CRISPY OVEN-FRIED CHICKEN WITH SAGE GRAVY

PREP 15 MIN • **BAKE/COOK** 45 MIN • **SERVES** 4

$1/2$ cup + 2 tablespoons all-purpose flour

2 egg whites, lightly beaten

$1^{1}/3$ cups cornflake crumbs

2 bone-in chicken breast halves, skinned

2 chicken drumsticks, skinned

2 chicken thighs, skinned

$1/2$ teaspoon salt

$1/8$ teaspoon cayenne

$1/4$ cup fat-free buttermilk

1 tablespoon butter

1 cup reduced-sodium chicken broth

$1/4$ teaspoon dried sage

$1/8$ teaspoon black pepper

1 Preheat the oven to 375°F. Line a large shallow baking pan with foil. Place a wire rack in the pan; spray the rack with nonstick spray.

2 Place $1/2$ cup of the flour in a shallow dish. Place the egg whites in another shallow dish. Place the cornflake crumbs in a third shallow dish.

3 Place the chicken in a large bowl; sprinkle with the salt and cayenne. Add the buttermilk and turn to coat. Dip the chicken, one piece at a time, into the flour, then into the egg whites, then into the cornflake crumbs, pressing to adhere. Place the chicken on the rack. Spray the top of the chicken lightly with nonstick spray. Bake until golden brown and cooked through, about 45 minutes (do not turn).

▸ **Filling Extra**
Serve with steamed green beans, bell peppers, and zucchini.

4 Meanwhile, to make the gravy, melt the butter in a small saucepan over medium-high heat. Whisk in the remaining 2 tablespoons flour; cook, whisking constantly, 1 minute. Gradually whisk in the chicken broth. Cook, whisking constantly, until the gravy comes to a boil and thickens, about 2 minutes. Stir in the sage and pepper. Divide chicken among 4 plates and serve with the gravy.

PER SERVING ($1/4$ of chicken with $1/4$ cup gravy): 310 Cal, 11 g Fat, 4 g Sat Fat, 0 g Trans Fat, 91 mg Chol, 635 mg Sod, 20 g Carb, 1 g Fib, 32 g Prot, 48 mg Calc. **POINTS** value: **7.**

TANDOORI CHICKEN

PREP 15 MIN • **BAKE** 25 MIN • **SERVES** 4

- 1 cup + $^1/_2$ cup plain fat-free yogurt
- 2 tablespoons lime juice
- 1$^1/_2$ tablespoons paprika
- 1 tablespoon grated peeled fresh ginger
- 2 garlic cloves, minced
- 2 teaspoons curry powder
- 4 ($^1/_4$-pound) skinless, boneless chicken thighs, trimmed
- $^1/_2$ medium cucumber, peeled, seeded, and grated
- $^1/_2$ teaspoon salt

1 Combine 1 cup of the yogurt, lime juice, paprika, ginger, garlic, and curry powder in a zip-close plastic bag; add the chicken. Squeeze out the air and seal the bag; turn to coat the chicken. Refrigerate, turning the bag occasionally, at least 1 hour or up to 8 hours.

2 Meanwhile, stir the remaining $^1/_2$ cup yogurt and cucumber together in a small bowl. Cover and refrigerate until ready to serve.

3 Preheat the oven to 450°F. Line a large shallow baking pan with foil. Place a wire rack in the pan; spray the rack with nonstick spray.

4 Remove the chicken from the marinade, sprinkle with the salt and place on the rack. Discard the marinade. Bake until the chicken is cooked through, 25–30 minutes. Serve with the yogurt sauce.

> ◗ **Filling Extra**
> Serve this dish with steamed broccoli. This recipe works with the **Simply Filling technique.**

PER SERVING (1 chicken thigh with about 2 tablespoons sauce): 213 Cal, 9 g Fat, 3 g Sat Fat, 0 g Trans Fat, 71 mg Chol, 393 mg Sod, 5 g Carb, 0 g Fib, 26 g Prot, 123 mg Calc. **POINTS** value: **5.**

BAKED STRIPED BASS WITH BACON BREAD CRUMBS

PREP 5 MIN • COOK/BAKE 20 MIN • SERVES 4

2   strips turkey bacon, chopped

2   tablespoons minced shallot

$1/2$ cup panko bread crumbs

1   teaspoon grated lemon zest

$1/2$ teaspoon salt

$1/4$ teaspoon black pepper

4   (5-ounce) skinless striped bass fillets or other firm-fleshed whitefish fillets

4   teaspoons reduced-fat mayonnaise

1 Preheat the oven to 425°F.

2 Spray a large ovenproof nonstick skillet with nonstick spray and set over medium-high heat. Add the bacon and shallot and cook, stirring occasionally, until the shallot is softened, about 5 minutes. Transfer to a bowl; stir in the bread crumbs, lemon zest, salt, and pepper.

3 Spread the fish fillets with the mayonnaise and place in the same skillet. Top the fillets with the bacon mixture. Bake until the fish is just opaque throughout, 12–15 minutes.

▶ **Filling Extra**
Accompany each serving of the fish with 1 cup of steamed spinach.

PER SERVING (1 fillet): 233 Cal, 8 g Fat, 2 g Sat Fat, 0 g Trans Fat, 77 mg Chol, 627 mg Sod, 7 g Carb, 0 g Fib, 31 g Prot, 51 mg Calc. *POINTS* value: *5.*

BAKED CRISPY SHRIMP WITH GRITS AND GREENS

PREP 15 MIN • **BAKE/COOK** 25 MIN • **SERVES** 4

$^1/_3$ **cup cornmeal**

$^1/_2$ **teaspoon smoked paprika**

$^1/_2$ **teaspoon dried thyme**

$^3/_4$ **teaspoon salt**

$^1/_2$ **teaspoon black pepper**

2 **large egg whites, lightly beaten**

1 **pound large shrimp, peeled and deveined**

2 **cups reduced-sodium chicken broth**

$^1/_2$ **cup quick-cooking grits**

$^1/_2$ **large red onion, thinly sliced**

1 **pound collard greens, thinly sliced**

1 Preheat the oven to 475°F. Line a baking sheet with foil and lightly spray the foil with nonstick spray.

2 Combine the cornmeal, paprika, thyme, $^1/_4$ teaspoon of the salt, and $^1/_4$ teaspoon of the pepper on a piece of wax paper. Place the egg whites in a shallow dish. Dip the shrimp into the egg whites, then into the cornmeal mixture. Arrange in a single layer on the baking sheet and spray lightly with nonstick spray. Bake until the shrimp are just opaque in the center, 8–10 minutes.

3 Meanwhile, bring the broth to a boil in a medium saucepan over medium-high heat. Gradually stir in the grits and cook, stirring frequently, until grits are thick and smooth, about 5 minutes.

4 Spray a large nonstick skillet with olive oil nonstick spray and set over medium-high heat. Add the onion and cook, stirring frequently, until softened, 5 minutes. Stir in the collard greens and the remaining $^1/_2$ teaspoon salt and $^1/_4$ teaspoon pepper. Cook, stirring occasionally, until crisp-tender, 5 minutes. Serve with the shrimp and grits.

In the Kitchen
You can coat the shrimp several hours ahead of time and cover and refrigerate until you're ready to bake them. This recipe works with the **Simply Filling technique.**

PER SERVING (5 shrimp, $^1/_2$ cup collards, and $^1/_3$ cup grits): 245 Cal, 3 g Fat, 0 g Sat Fat, 0 g Trans Fat, 107 mg Chol, 898 mg Sod, 35 g Carb, 5 g Fib, 21 g Prot, 209 mg Calc. **POINTS** value: **4.**

BEAN AND CORN CASSEROLE WITH TORTILLA-CRUNCH TOPPING

PREP 15 MIN • COOK/BAKE 35 MIN • SERVES 4

1 medium onion, thinly sliced
1 red bell pepper, thinly sliced
2 garlic cloves, minced
1 (12-ounce) bag thawed frozen corn
1 (4-ounce) can diced green chiles
2 large eggs
3 large egg whites

1/4 cup low-fat (1%) milk
1/2 teaspoon hot pepper sauce
1/2 cup part-skim ricotta
1 (15 1/2-ounce) can black beans, rinsed and drained
1/2 cup shredded low-fat Mexican cheese blend
12 baked low-fat tortilla chips, crumbled

1 Preheat the oven to 375°F. Spray a 2-quart baking dish with nonstick spray.

2 Spray a large nonstick skillet with nonstick spray and set over medium-high heat. Add the onion and pepper and cook, stirring frequently, until softened, 5 minutes. Add the garlic and cook, stirring constantly, until fragrant, about 30 seconds. Remove from the heat and stir in the corn and chiles.

▸ Filling Extra
Add 2 chopped plum tomatoes when you stir in the beans in step 3.

3 Whisk the eggs, egg whites, milk, pepper sauce, and ricotta together in a large bowl. Stir in the beans and the vegetable mixture. Spoon into the baking dish and top evenly with the cheese. Sprinkle with the chips and bake until golden brown and bubbly, 30–35 minutes.

PER SERVING (1/4 of casserole): 363 Cal, 10 g Fat, 4 g Sat Fat, 0 g Trans Fat, 124 mg Chol, 785 mg Sod, 50 g Carb, 12 g Fib, 22 g Prot, 327 mg Calc. *POINTS* value: *7.*

CRISPY UNFRIED FISH AND CHIPS

PREP 15 MIN • BAKE 30 MIN • SERVES 4

- 2 large (8-ounce) russet potatoes, scrubbed
- 1 teaspoon salt
- $1/2$ teaspoon paprika
- 2 tablespoons sliced almonds
- $1/4$ cup panko bread crumbs
- $1/4$ cup cornmeal
- 2 large egg whites
- 1 tablespoon whole-grain mustard
- 2 (8-ounce) tilapia fillets, each cut into 4 pieces

1 Preheat the oven to 475°F.

2 Halve the potatoes and cut each piece lengthwise into quarters. Place on a medium rimmed nonstick baking sheet. Spray lightly with olive oil nonstick spray and sprinkle with $1/2$ teaspoon of the salt and the paprika. Arrange the potatoes in a single layer and bake until the bottoms are deep golden and crisp, about 15 minutes. Turn the potatoes onto the opposite cut side and bake until crisp, 10–15 minutes longer.

3 Meanwhile, to make the fish, spray another medium rimmed baking sheet with nonstick spray.

4 Put the almonds in a food processor and pulse until finely ground. Add the bread crumbs and cornmeal and pulse until well combined. Spread the mixture on a piece of wax paper. Whisk the egg whites and mustard together in a shallow dish.

In the Kitchen
Try using smoked paprika instead of regular paprika to give the potatoes a subtle smoky flavor.

5 Sprinkle the fish with the remaining $1/2$ teaspoon salt. Dip each piece into the egg white mixture, then into the almond mixture, pressing to adhere. Place the fish on the baking sheet and bake until the fish is golden brown and just opaque in the center, 6–8 minutes.

PER SERVING (2 pieces fish and 4 potato wedges): 319 Cal, 4 g Fat, 1 g Sat Fat, 0 g Trans Fat, 60 mg Chol, 791 mg Sod, 43 g Carb, 5 g Fib, 28 g Prot, 71 mg Calc. **POINTS** value: **6.**

CRISPY UNFRIED
FISH AND CHIPS

Penne with Oven-Roasted Tomatoes and Balsamic Syrup

PREP 10 MIN • BAKE/COOK 30 MIN • SERVES 4

2   cups grape tomatoes, halved

1/2 teaspoon salt

1/2 teaspoon black pepper

1   cup balsamic vinegar

2   cups whole-wheat penne

1   tablespoon extra-virgin olive oil

1/4 cup thinly sliced fresh basil leaves

1/2 cup freshly shaved ricotta salata

1 Preheat the oven to 450°F. Spray a large rimmed baking sheet with nonstick spray. Place the tomatoes on the baking sheet and spray lightly with nonstick spray. Sprinkle with 1/4 teaspoon of the salt and the pepper. Bake until softened, 30 minutes, stirring every 10 minutes.

2 Meanwhile, place the vinegar in a small saucepan and bring to a boil over high heat; boil, stirring occasionally, until reduced to about 1/4 cup, about 15 minutes.

3 Cook the penne according to the package directions, omitting the salt if desired. Drain, reserving 2 tablespoons of the cooking liquid.

In the Kitchen
Make an extra batch of the balsamic syrup in this recipe to use as a fat-free dressing for pasta or green salads.

4 Transfer the pasta to a large bowl; add the reserved pasta cooking water, tomatoes, olive oil, basil, and remaining 1/4 teaspoon salt and toss to combine. Divide the pasta mixture among 4 plates; drizzle evenly with the vinegar and sprinkle with the cheese.

PER SERVING (1 1/4 cups): 333 Cal, 9 g Fat, 4 g Sat Fat, 0 g Trans Fat, 17 mg Chol, 245 mg Sod, 49 g Carb, 7 g Fib, 13 g Prot, 126 mg Calc. ***POINTS*** value: ***7.***

Easy Layered Ravioli Bake

1   (9-ounce) package refrigerated low-fat cheese ravioli

1   (24-ounce) jar fat-free marinara sauce

2   (10-ounce) packages frozen chopped spinach, thawed and squeezed dry

1   cup shredded part-skim mozzarella

2   tablespoons grated Parmesan

1 Preheat the oven to 375°F.

2 Cook the ravioli according to the package directions, omitting the oil and salt if desired.

3 Spray a 2-quart baking dish with nonstick spray. Spread half the marinara sauce in the dish. Add half of the ravioli, then top with half of the spinach and half of the mozzarella. Repeat layering once. Sprinkle with the Parmesan. Cover with foil and bake until bubbly, about 20 minutes. Uncover and bake until the cheese is melted and slightly golden, 6–8 minutes longer.

PER SERVING (1/4 of casserole): 340 Cal, 10 g Fat, 6 g Sat Fat, 0 g Trans Fat, 46 mg Chol, 1,133 mg Sod, 42 g Carb, 7 g Fib, 23 g Prot, 485 mg Calc. *POINTS* value: *7.*

UPSIDE-DOWN VEGGIE PIZZA PIE

PREP 15 MIN • **COOK/BAKE** 25 MIN • **SERVES** 6

1 yellow bell pepper, thinly sliced
1 green bell pepper, thinly sliced
1 small red onion, thinly sliced
1 clove garlic, minced

1½ cups shredded part-skim mozzarella
1 pound refrigerated or thawed frozen pizza dough
¼ cup grated Parmesan

1 Place an oven rack on the bottom rung of the oven. Preheat the oven to 450°F.

2 Spray a 12-inch cast-iron skillet with nonstick spray and set over medium-high heat. Add the peppers, onion, and garlic and cook, stirring occasionally, until tender, 5 minutes. Remove from the heat and sprinkle with the mozzarella.

3 Sprinkle a work surface lightly with flour. Turn the pizza dough onto the surface; with a lightly floured rolling pin, roll into a 12-inch circle. Place the dough in the skillet, covering the vegetable mixture. Prick the dough in several places with a fork and lightly spray with nonstick spray.

4 Bake on the bottom rack of the oven until the crust is golden, 20 minutes. To loosen, run a thin knife around the side of the skillet. Invert the pizza onto a serving plate. Sprinkle with the Parmesan and cut into 6 wedges.

PER SERVING (⅙ of pizza): 309 Cal, 11 g Fat, 5 g Sat Fat, 0 g Trans Fat, 18 mg Chol, 546 mg Sod, 38 g Carb, 2 g Fib, 14 g Prot, 278 mg Calc. *POINTS* value: *7.*

Fresh Green Bean Casserole

PREP 15 MIN • COOK/BAKE 40 MIN • SERVES 4

3/4 pound green beans, trimmed

2 teaspoons olive oil

1 (8-ounce) package sliced fresh mushrooms

1 medium onion, chopped

2 garlic cloves, minced

1/4 cup dry Madeira or reduced-sodium chicken broth

1 tablespoon all-purpose flour

1 cup reduced-sodium chicken broth

1/2 teaspoon salt

1/8 teaspoon black pepper

2/3 cup fresh bread crumbs

5 teaspoons light butter, melted

1 tablespoon grated Parmesan

1 Preheat the oven to 350°F. Spray a 1 1/2-quart baking dish with nonstick spray.

2 Bring a large saucepan of lightly salted water to a boil. Add the beans; return to a boil and cook until just crisp-tender, 2 minutes. Drain.

3 Heat the oil in a large nonstick skillet over medium-high heat. Add the mushrooms and onion and cook, stirring occasionally, until lightly browned, 6–7 minutes. Add the garlic and cook, stirring constantly, until fragrant, about 30 seconds. Add the Madeira and cook until evaporated, about 1 minute. Add the flour and cook, stirring constantly, 1 minute.

> ❯ **Filling Extra**
> Make this a complete meal by serving the green beans with ham (a 3-ounce slice of cooked lean ham per serving will increase the **POINTS** value by **3**).

4 Add the broth and cook, stirring constantly, until the mixture comes to a boil and thickens, about 2 minutes. Remove from the heat and stir in the beans, salt, and pepper. Pour into the prepared baking dish.

5 Stir the bread crumbs, butter, and cheese together in a small bowl until blended. Sprinkle the crumb mixture over the casserole and bake, uncovered, until the casserole is bubbly and the top is golden, 20 minutes.

PER SERVING (1 1/2 cups): 134 Cal, 6 g Fat, 2 g Sat Fat, 0 g Trans Fat, 7 mg Chol, 544 mg Sod, 17 g Carb, 4 g Fib, 6 g Prot, 77 mg Calc. **POINTS** value: **2.**

30
MINUTES
OR LESS

Chapter 7

GRILLED SPICE-RUBBED T-BONE STEAK

PREP 5 MIN • **GRILL** 10 MIN • **SERVES** 4

$1/2$ **teaspoon ground cumin**
$1/2$ **teaspoon ground coriander**
$1/2$ **teaspoon salt**

$1/2$ **teaspoon smoked paprika**
$1/4$ **teaspoon black pepper**
1 **($1^1/4$-pound) T-bone steak, trimmed**

1 Combine the cumin, coriander, salt, paprika, and pepper in a small bowl. Rub the mixture on both sides of the steak.

2 Spray a nonstick ridged grill pan with nonstick spray and set over medium-high heat. Add the steak and cook, turning once, until an instant-read thermometer inserted in the side of the beef registers 145°F for medium-rare, 8–10 minutes. Transfer the steak to a cutting board; let stand 5 minutes. Cut into thin slices.

◗ Filling Extra
Serve this spicy steak with a fresh salsa made with chopped tomatoes, minced red onion, jalapeño, cilantro, and lime juice. This recipe works with the **Simply Filling technique.**

PER SERVING (¼ of steak): 165 Cal, 7 g Fat, 3 g Sat Fat, 0 g Trans Fat, 46 mg Chol, 328 mg Sod, 0 g Carb, 0 g Fib, 24 g Prot, 11 mg Calc. **POINTS** value: **4.**

STEAK SALAD WITH BLUE CHEESE AND WALNUTS

PREP 10 MIN • COOK 10 MIN • SERVES 4

1   (1-pound) flank steak, trimmed
3/4 teaspoon salt
1/4 teaspoon black pepper
1   tablespoon red-wine vinegar
2   teaspoons extra-virgin olive oil

1   teaspoon Dijon mustard
1   (5-ounce) container mixed baby greens
1/2 small red onion, thinly sliced
2   tablespoons crumbled blue cheese
2   tablespoons toasted chopped walnuts

1 Spray a large nonstick skillet with nonstick spray and set over medium-high heat. Sprinkle the steak with 1/2 teaspoon salt and the pepper. Place the steak in the skillet and cook, turning once, until an instant-read thermometer inserted into the side of the steak registers 145°F for medium-rare, 8–10 minutes. Transfer the steak to a cutting board and let stand 5 minutes. Cut the steak against the grain into 12 slices.

2 Meanwhile, to make the salad, whisk the vinegar, oil, mustard, and remaining 1/4 teaspoon salt in a large bowl until blended. Add the greens, onion, blue cheese, and walnuts and toss to coat. Divide the salad evenly among 4 plates and top with the steak.

PER SERVING (1 salad): 248 Cal, 10 g Fat, 3 g Sat Fat, 0 g Trans Fat, 85 mg Chol, 584 mg Sod, 3 g Carb, 1 g Fib, 35 g Prot, 50 mg Calc. **POINTS** value: **6.**

OPEN-FACE PHILLY CHEESESTEAK SANDWICHES

PREP 10 MIN • COOK/BROIL 15 MIN • SERVES 4

2   teaspoons olive oil
$^1/_2$ pound top round steak cut into thin strips
1   green bell pepper, thinly sliced
1   onion, thinly sliced
2   garlic cloves, chopped

1   tablespoon Worcestershire sauce
$^1/_2$ teaspoon hot sauce
$^1/_4$ teaspoon salt
4   slices whole-grain peasant bread
4   ($^1/_2$-ounce) slices Jarlsberg or Swiss cheese

1 Preheat the boiler. Spray a broiler rack with nonstick spray.

2 Heat 1 teaspoon of the oil in a large nonstick skillet over medium-high heat. Add the beef and cook, turning occasionally, until browned, 3–4 minutes. Transfer to a plate. Add the remaining 1 teaspoon oil to the skillet. Add the bell pepper, onion, and garlic and cook, stirring occasionally, until the vegetables are softened, 8 minutes. Stir in the beef, Worcestershire, hot sauce, and salt; cook until heated through, 2 minutes.

3 Spoon $^1/_2$ cup of the steak mixture onto each bread slice and top with the cheese. Place on the broiler rack and broil until the cheese is melted and bubbly, 1–2 minutes.

PER SERVING (1 sandwich): 234 Cal, 9 g Fat, 4 g Sat Fat, 0 g Trans Fat, 44 mg Chol, 384 mg Sod, 18 g Carb, 3 g Fib, 20 g Prot, 161 mg Calc. **POINTS** value: **5.**

OPEN-FACE PHILLY CHEESESTEAK
SANDWICHES

FAST FRENCH DIP SANDWICHES

PREP 10 MIN • COOK 10 MIN • SERVES 4

2   teaspoons olive oil

1   shallot, thinly sliced

2   teaspoons all-purpose flour

1   cup reduced-sodium beef broth

1   teaspoon chopped fresh thyme

Pinch black pepper

1   (8-ounce) loaf whole-wheat French bread

³/₄ pound thinly sliced rare deli roast beef

1 To make the sauce, heat the oil in a small nonstick saucepan over medium heat. Add the shallot and cook, stirring frequently, until softened, 3 minutes. Sprinkle the shallots with the flour and cook, stirring constantly, 1 minute. Add the broth and bring to a boil. Reduce the heat and simmer, uncovered, stirring occasionally, until the sauce thickens slightly, 3 minutes. Remove from the heat and stir in the thyme and pepper. Keep warm.

> **Filling Extra**
> Serve these sandwiches with a salad made with iceberg lettuce, halved cherry tomatoes and chopped cucumbers tossed with red-wine vinegar, salt, and pepper.

2 Meanwhile, preheat the broiler. Slice the bread horizontally, almost all the way through, and spread apart. Place the bread on a baking sheet and broil until toasted, 1–2 minutes. Place the beef on a plate and cover with a damp paper towel and microwave on High until just heated through, 1 minute. Arrange the beef in the bread and cut into four sandwiches. Serve with the sauce for dipping.

PER SERVING (1 sandwich with about 3 tablespoons sauce): 278 Cal, 7 g Fat, 2 g Sat Fat, 1 g Trans Fat, 42 mg Chol, 1,184 mg Sod, 28 g Carb, 4 g Fib, 26 g Prot, 70 mg Calc. **POINTS** value: **5.**

SPICY CHICKEN KEBABS WITH ONIONS, MUSHROOMS, AND PEPPERS

PREP 20 MIN • GRILL 10 MIN • SERVES 4

1/4 cup chopped fresh cilantro

2 teaspoons canola oil

2 teaspoons grated lime zest

2 tablespoons lime juice

1 clove garlic, minced

1 teaspoon ground cumin

1/2 teaspoon salt

1/8 teaspoon cayenne

1 pound skinless, boneless chicken breast, cut into cubes

1 red bell pepper, cut into 1-inch pieces

1 yellow bell pepper, cut into 1-inch pieces

1 sweet onion, cut into 8 wedges

8 ounces small whole mushrooms, stems removed

Lime wedges

1 Spray the grill rack with nonstick spray; preheat the grill to medium-high or prepare a medium fire.

2 Stir the cilantro, oil, lime zest, lime juice, garlic, cumin, salt, and cayenne together in a large bowl; add the chicken, bell peppers, onion, and mushrooms; toss to coat. Thread onto 8 (8-inch) metal skewers.

3 Grill the skewers, turning frequently, until browned and cooked through, 10–12 minutes. Serve with the lime wedges.

> **Filling Extra**
> Serve the kebabs atop cooked brown rice (1/2 cup per serving will increase the **POINTS** value by **2**). This recipe works with the **Simply Filling technique.**

PER SERVING (2 kebabs): 211 Cal, 6 g Fat, 1 g Sat Fat, 0 g Trans Fat, 70 mg Chol, 367 mg Sod, 10 g Carb, 2 g Fib, 28 g Prot, 39 mg Calc. **POINTS** value: **4.**

HORSERADISH
HAMBURGERS

HORSERADISH HAMBURGERS

1   pound lean ground beef (5% fat or less)
2   scallions, finely chopped
1/4   cup finely shredded carrot
1   tablespoon prepared horseradish
1/2   teaspoon salt

4   multigrain hamburger buns, split and toasted
4   green leaf lettuce leaves
4   tablespoons ketchup (optional)
4   slices tomato
1/2   cup shredded red cabbage

1 Stir the beef, scallions, carrot, horseradish, and salt together in a medium bowl until well mixed. Form into 4 patties.

2 Spray a nonstick ridged grill pan with nonstick spray and set over medium-high heat. Add the patties and cook until an instant-read thermometer inserted into the side of a burger registers 160°F for well done, 4–5 minutes on each side.

3 Spread the cut sides of the buns with ketchup, if using. Place the burgers in the buns and top evenly with the lettuce leaves, tomato slices, and cabbage.

In the Kitchen
Adding shredded carrot and chopped scallions to these burgers adds flavor and helps keep them moist while cooking.

PER SERVING (1 garnished burger without ketchup): 249 Cal, 7 g Fat, 3 g Sat Fat, 0 g Trans Fat, 60 mg Chol, 484 mg Sod, 20 g Carb, 2 g Fib, 27 g Prot, 72 mg Calc. *POINTS* value: *5.*

JERK CHICKEN THIGHS WITH FRESH PINEAPPLE SALSA

PREP 15 MIN • **GRILL** 15 MIN • **SERVES** 4

4   scallions, chopped

¹/₄ cup lime juice

¹/₄ cup lightly packed fresh cilantro leaves

2   tablespoons + 1 teaspoon sugar

1   tablespoon low-sodium soy sauce

2   garlic cloves

2   quarter-size slices peeled fresh ginger

2   jalapeño peppers, seeded and chopped

1   teaspoon ground allspice

¹/₄ teaspoon cinnamon

4   (1¹/₄-pound) skinless, boneless chicken thighs, trimmed

¹/₂ peeled and cored pineapple, diced

¹/₂ small red onion, finely chopped

1   tablespoon apple-cider vinegar

1   tablespoon chopped fresh cilantro

¹/₂ teaspoon salt

1 Place the scallions, lime juice, packed cilantro leaves, 2 tablespoons of the sugar, soy sauce, garlic, ginger, jalapeños, allspice, and cinnamon in a blender and process until smooth. Transfer to a zip-close plastic bag; add the chicken. Squeeze out the air and seal the bag; turn to coat the chicken. Refrigerate, turning the bag occasionally, at least 1 hour or up to 8 hours.

In the Kitchen
Use this delicious jerk marinade for skinless boneless chicken breasts and boneless center-cut pork loin chops too.

2 Meanwhile, to make the salsa, stir the pineapple, onion, vinegar, chopped cilantro, and remaining 1 teaspoon sugar together in a medium bowl. Cover and refrigerate until ready to use.

3 Spray the grill rack with nonstick spray; preheat the grill to medium-high or prepare a medium-hot fire.

4 Remove the chicken from the marinade, sprinkle with the salt, and place on the grill rack. Discard the marinade. Grill the chicken, turning occasionally, until cooked through, 12–15 minutes. Serve with the salsa.

PER SERVING (1 chicken thigh and ¹/₂ cup salsa): 258 Cal, 9 g Fat, 3 g Sat Fat, 0 g Trans Fat, 70 mg Chol, 394 mg Sod, 20 g Carb, 2 g Fib, 25 g Prot, 49 mg Calc. ***POINTS*** value: **6.**

CHEESE-STUFFED CHICKEN BURGERS

PREP 10 MIN • COOK 15 MIN • SERVES 4

³/₄ cup shredded reduced-fat sharp cheddar

1 tablespoon Dijon mustard

1 pound ground chicken breast

¹/₃ cup plain dried bread crumbs

¹/₄ teaspoon salt

4 light multigrain English muffins, split and toasted

¹/₄ cup ketchup

4 lettuce leaves

4 tomato slices

12 bread and butter pickle slices

1 Stir the cheese and mustard together in a small bowl. Stir the chicken, bread crumbs, and salt together in a medium bowl just until blended. Form into 4 balls. With your index finger, make a deep indentation in each ball. Fill each indentation with 3 tablespoons of the cheese mixture. Fold the chicken mixture around the cheese to seal; shape each one into a 3-inch-diameter patty.

2 Spray a nonstick ridged grill pan with nonstick spray and set over medium heat. Place the burgers in the pan and cook until an instant-read thermometer inserted into the side of each burger (without touching the cheese) registers 165°F, 6–7 minutes on each side.

3 Serve the burgers in the muffins topped with the ketchup, lettuce leaves, tomato slices, and pickles.

> ◗ **Filling Extra**
> Top the burgers with sliced roasted red bell peppers. If using bottled roasted red peppers, select peppers that are not packed in oil.

PER SERVING (1 burger): 393 Cal, 7 g Fat, 2 g Sat Fat, 2 g Trans Fat, 75 mg Chol, 1,155 mg Sod, 43 g Carb, 5 g Fib, 39 g Prot, 377 mg Calc. *POINTS* value: **8.**

Glazed Ham-and–Sweet Potato Kebabs

PREP 10 MIN • COOK 15 MIN • SERVES 4

2   sweet potatoes, peeled and cut into
    1-inch pieces
1/4 cup peach preserves
1   tablespoon Dijon mustard

1   garlic clove, minced
1   (3/4-pound) ham steak, trimmed and cut into
    1-inch pieces
2   green bell peppers, cut into 1-inch pieces

1 Bring the potatoes and enough water to cover in a large saucepan to a boil. Reduce the heat and simmer, until the potatoes are almost tender, 8–10 minutes. Drain and let cool slightly.

2 Meanwhile, to make the glaze, combine the preserves, mustard, and garlic in a small bowl. Thread the potatoes, ham, and bell peppers alternately onto 8 (8-inch) metal skewers. Brush the kebabs with half of the glaze.

3 Spray a large nonstick ridged grill pan with nonstick spray and set over medium heat. Add the kebabs and cook, turning often and brushing with the remaining glaze, until the ham is browned and heated through, 5–6 minutes. Cook in 2 batches if necessary.

In the Kitchen
If using wooden skewers be sure to soak them in water for 30 minutes before using.

PER SERVING (2 kebabs): 239 Cal, 6 g Fat, 2 g Sat Fat, 0 g Trans Fat, 36 mg Chol, 1,044 mg Sod, 30 g Carb, 3 g Fib, 16 g Prot, 39 mg Calc. **POINTS** value: **5.**

GLAZED HAM-AND–SWEET POTATO KEBABS

Pizza with Sun-Dried-Tomato Sausage and Peppers

PREP 10 MIN • COOK/BAKE 20 MIN • SERVES 4

2 (3-ounce) fully cooked sun-dried-tomato chicken sausages, sliced

1 (8-ounce) package sliced mushrooms

1/2 small red bell pepper, thinly sliced

2 garlic cloves, thinly sliced

1 (10-ounce) thin whole-wheat pizza crust

1 cup fat-free tomato-basil pasta sauce

3/4 cup shredded fat-free mozzarella

1 tablespoon grated Parmesan

1 Place an oven rack on the bottom rung of the oven. Preheat the oven to 425°F.

2 Spray a medium nonstick skillet with nonstick spray and set over medium-high heat. Add the sausage and cook, stirring occasionally, until lightly browned, 3–4 minutes. Transfer to a plate. Add the mushrooms and bell pepper to the skillet; cook, stirring occasionally, until softened, 5 minutes. Stir in the garlic and cook 1 minute longer. Remove from the heat.

3 Place the crust on a baking sheet. Spread evenly with the pasta sauce; top with the mozzarella, sausage, and the mushroom mixture. Sprinkle with the Parmesan. Bake until the crust is crisp and the cheese is melted, 8–10 minutes. Cut into 8 wedges.

PER SERVING (1/4 of pizza): 352 Cal, 10 g Fat, 4 g Sat Fat, 0 g Trans Fat, 30 mg Chol, 1,124 mg Sod, 46 g Carb, 6 g Fib, 25 g Prot, 324 mg Calc. **POINTS** value: **7.**

GRILLED TUNA SOUVLAKI
WITH YOGURT SAUCE

PREP 15 MIN • **GRILL** 10 MIN • **SERVES** 4

1 cup shredded cucumber

$1/2$ cup finely chopped fennel bulb

1 teaspoon salt

1 cup plain fat-free Greek yogurt

$1^1/2$ tablespoons red-wine vinegar

2 teaspoons extra-virgin olive oil

2 garlic cloves, minced

1 pound tuna steak, cut into 1-inch chunks

1 yellow or red bell pepper, cut into 1-inch pieces

$1/2$ large red onion, cut into 1-inch pieces

1 teaspoon dried oregano

$1/2$ teaspoon black pepper

4 mini whole-wheat pita breads

1 Spray the grill rack with nonstick spray. Preheat the grill to medium-high or prepare a medium-high fire.

2 To make the sauce, place the cucumber and fennel in a colander over a bowl; sprinkle with $1/2$ teaspoon of the salt and toss to combine. Let stand to drain. Stir the yogurt, vinegar, olive oil, and 1 of the garlic cloves together in a medium bowl; set aside.

3 Toss the tuna, bell pepper, onion, remaining 1 garlic clove, remaining $1/2$ teaspoon salt, oregano, and pepper together in a large bowl. Lightly spray with olive oil nonstick spray and toss to coat. Alternately thread onto 4 (10- to 12-inch) metal skewers.

4 Place the kebabs on the grill rack and grill until the tuna is slightly pink in the center, 3–5 minutes on each side. Place the pita bread on the grill rack and grill until warmed, 1 minute on each side.

5 Squeeze the excess moisture from the cucumber mixture and stir into the yogurt mixture. Serve with the kebabs and pita breads.

PER SERVING (1 kebab with $1/3$ cup sauce and 1 pita bread): 309 Cal, 9 g Fat, 2 g Sat Fat, 0 g Trans Fat, 68 mg Chol, 643 mg Sod, 28 g Carb, 4 g Fib, 29 g Prot, 179 mg Calc. **POINTS** value: **6.**

Tuna Melts with Spinach and Jarlsberg

PREP 10 MIN • BROIL 5 MIN • SERVES 4

1 (6-ounce) can albacore tuna packed in water, drained and broken into chunks

$1/4$ cup reduced-fat mayonnaise

1 stalk celery, finely chopped

2 tablespoons finely chopped scallion

1 tablespoon lemon juice

$1/4$ teaspoon salt

$1/4$ teaspoon black pepper

2 drops hot pepper sauce

2 whole-wheat English muffins, split and toasted

1 cup baby spinach

4 slices tomato

4 ($3/4$-ounce) slices Jarlsberg

1 Preheat the broiler.

2 Stir the tuna, mayonnaise, celery, scallion, lemon juice, salt, pepper, and pepper sauce together in a medium bowl.

3 Top each muffin half with $1/4$ cup of the spinach; top evenly with the tuna mixture, a tomato slice, and a cheese slice.

4 Place the sandwiches on a baking sheet. Broil 5 inches from the heat until the cheese melts, about 2 minutes.

In the Kitchen
You can substitute peppery greens like arugula or watercress for the spinach if you prefer a little spiciness.

PER SERVING (1 open-face sandwich): 227 Cal, 9 g Fat, 4 g Sat Fat, 0 g Trans Fat, 31 mg Chol, 616 mg Sod, 18 g Carb, 3 g Fib, 19 g Prot, 277 mg Calc. **POINTS** value: **5.**

GRILLED SCALLOP KEBABS WITH CURRIED RICE PILAF

PREP 15 MIN • COOK/GRILL 25 MIN • SERVES 4

2   teaspoons canola oil
1   large onion, chopped
1   cup basmati rice
1   teaspoon curry powder
1³/₄ cups reduced-sodium chicken broth
1   teaspoon salt

¹/₂   teaspoon black pepper
2   tablespoons golden raisins
2   tablespoons chopped fresh cilantro
1   pound sea scallops
1   large peach, pitted and sliced
1¹/₂ cups cherry tomatoes

1 Spray the grill rack with nonstick spray. Preheat the grill to medium-high or prepare a medium-high fire.

2 Heat the oil in a medium saucepan over medium-high heat. Add the onion and cook, stirring frequently, until it begins to soften, 3 minutes. Stir in the rice and curry powder. Add the broth, ¹/₂ teaspoon of the salt, and ¹/₄ teaspoon of the pepper and bring to a boil. Reduce the heat, cover, and simmer, until the rice is tender and the liquid is absorbed, 20 minutes. Stir in the raisins and cilantro and keep warm.

> **♦ Filling Extra**
> For a colorful accompaniment to the kebabs, grill 2 trimmed bunches of scallions. Place them on the grill and turn frequently, just until lightly charred, 2–3 minutes.

3 Meanwhile, thread the scallops, peach slices, and cherry tomatoes alternately onto 8 (6- to 8-inch) metal skewers. Sprinkle with the remaining ¹/₂ teaspoon salt and ¹/₄ teaspoon pepper and lightly spray with olive oil nonstick spray. Place the kebabs on the grill rack and grill until the scallops are opaque in the center, 2–3 minutes on each side. Serve with the pilaf.

PER SERVING (2 kebabs with ³/₄ cup pilaf): 314 Cal, 4 g Fat, 0 g Sat Fat, 0 g Trans Fat, 30 mg Chol, 990 mg Sod, 52 g Carb, 4 g Fib, 19 g Prot, 107 mg Calc. *POINTS* value: *6.*

FISH TACOS WITH CRUNCHY SLAW

FISH TACOS WITH CRUNCHY SLAW

PREP 15 MIN • BROIL 5 MIN • SERVES 4

$^1/_2$ cup light sour cream

1 teaspoon minced chipotles en adobo

4 cups coleslaw mix

1 teaspoon grated lime zest

$1^1/_2$ tablespoons lime juice

2 teaspoons canola oil

1 teaspoon salt

$^3/_4$ teaspoon black pepper

$^1/_2$ teaspoon chili powder

1 pound firm-fleshed skinless cod or halibut fillets, cut into 1-inch pieces

8 (6-inch) corn tortillas, warmed

1 Spray a broiler rack with nonstick spray and preheat the broiler.

2 Stir the sour cream and chipotles en adobo together in a small bowl.

3 Stir the coleslaw mix, lime zest, lime juice, oil, $^1/_2$ teaspoon of the salt, and $^1/_2$ teaspoon of the pepper together in a large bowl.

> **▶ Filling Extra**
> Top the tortillas with chopped tomatoes and thinly sliced scallions.

4 Sprinkle the fish with the remaining $^1/_2$ teaspoon salt, remaining $^1/_4$ teaspoon pepper, and the chili powder. Spray lightly with olive oil nonstick spray and place on the broiler rack. Broil 5 inches from the heat until the fish is just opaque throughout, 3–5 minutes. Divide the fish evenly among the tortillas. Top evenly with the slaw and the sour cream mixture.

PER SERVING (2 tacos): 297 Cal, 9 g Fat, 3 g Sat Fat, 0 g Trans Fat, 72 mg Chol, 750 mg Sod, 28 g Carb, 5 g Fib, 26 g Prot, 120 mg Calc. **POINTS** value: **6.**

SURF-AND-TURF PIZZA

PREP 10 MIN • **BAKE** 10 MIN • **SERVES** 4

- 1 tube (13.8 ounces) refrigerated pizza dough
- 1 (6$\frac{1}{2}$-ounce) can minced clams, drained
- 1 small zucchini, thinly sliced
- 1 ounce prosciutto, chopped
- $\frac{1}{2}$ cup grated Parmesan
- $\frac{1}{4}$ cup torn basil

1 Preheat the oven to 475°F.

2 Unroll the dough onto a pizza pan or a baking sheet, gently pulling on the dough to form a 12-inch circle. Sprinkle the dough evenly with the clams, zucchini, and prosciutto. Lightly spray the top of the pizza with olive oil cooking spray. Sprinkle with the Parmesan and bake until crisp and browned, 10–12 minutes. Sprinkle with the basil and cut into 8 wedges.

PER SERVING ($\frac{1}{4}$ of pizza): 335 Cal, 11 g Fat, 4 g Sat Fat, 0 g Trans Fat, 16 mg Chol, 705 mg Sod, 45 g Carb, 2 g Fib, 14 g Prot, 196 mg Calc. **POINTS** value: **7.**

STUFFED PORTOBELLO-CHEESE SANDWICHES

4   (4-inch) portobello mushrooms, stems discarded and caps wiped clean

$^1/_4$ cup sun-dried tomato halves (not packed in oil), chopped

$^1/_4$ cup chopped pitted kalamata olives

$^1/_4$ cup chopped fresh parsley

$^1/_4$ cup shredded fontina

2   garlic cloves, minced

$^1/_4$ teaspoon salt

$^1/_4$ teaspoon black pepper

2   tablespoons fresh whole-wheat bread crumbs

2   teaspoons olive oil

4   (4-inch) squares whole-wheat focaccia, toasted

1   small avocado, pitted, peeled, and sliced

1   small red onion, thinly sliced

1 Preheat the broiler. Spray a large rimmed baking sheet with nonstick spray. Place the mushrooms on the baking sheet and lightly spray with nonstick spray. Broil the mushrooms 4 inches from the heat until tender, turning once, 6–8 minutes.

2 Meanwhile, combine the tomatoes, olives, parsley, fontina, garlic, salt, and pepper in small bowl. Spoon the tomato mixture evenly into each mushroom cap; sprinkle evenly with the bread crumbs and drizzle with the oil.

3 Return the mushrooms to the broiler and broil until the cheese is melted and the bread crumbs are golden brown, about 1 minute.

4 Top each focaccia square with a mushroom, then top evenly with the avocado and onion.

◊ Filling Extra
Top the mushrooms with a few baby spinach or baby arugula leaves before adding the avocado and onion.

PER SERVING (1 open-face sandwich): 312 Cal, 12 g Fat, 3 g Sat Fat, 0 g Trans Fat, 8 mg Chol, 693 mg Sod, 40 g Carb, 8 g Fib, 10 g Prot, 118 mg Calc. *POINTS* value: **6.**

PRESTO POLENTA WITH GOAT CHEESE, CORN, TOMATOES, AND BASIL

PREP 10 MIN • **COOK** 15 MIN • **SERVES** 4

2   ears corn-on-the-cob, kernels removed
1   cup cherry tomatoes, quartered
$^1/_4$ cup thinly sliced fresh basil leaves
2   cups low-fat (1%) milk
2   cups reduced-sodium vegetable broth

$^1/_4$ teaspoon salt
$^1/_4$ teaspoon black pepper
1   cup instant polenta
$^1/_2$ cup crumbled goat cheese

1 Stir the corn, tomatoes and basil together in a medium bowl.

2 Combine the milk, vegetable broth, salt, and pepper in a large saucepan; bring to a boil over medium-high heat.

3 Slowly pour in the polenta in a thin, steady stream, whisking constantly. Cook, whisking constantly, until thick and creamy, 5–6 minutes. Divide the polenta among 4 plates; top each serving evenly with the corn mixture. Sprinkle evenly with the goat cheese.

PER SERVING (1$^1/_4$ cups polenta with $^1/_2$ cup tomato mixture and 2 tablespoons goat cheese): 324 Cal, 6 g Fat, 4 g Sat Fat, 0 g Trans Fat, 17 mg Chol, 511 mg Sod, 55 g Carb, 6 g Fib, 14 g Prot, 207 mg Calc. *POINTS* value: *6.*

PRESTO POLENTA WITH GOAT CHEESE, CORN, TOMATOES, AND BASIL

SIDES
TO GO WITH
DINNER

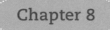

Chapter 8

BACON-CHEDDAR MASHED POTATOES

PREP 15 MIN • **COOK** 25 MIN • **SERVES** 4

1½ pounds russet potatoes, peeled and cut into 1-inch pieces

½ cup fat-free sour cream

2 tablespoons fat-free milk

⅛ teaspoon salt

⅛ teaspoon black pepper

⅓ cup shredded low-fat sharp cheddar

2 slices center-cut bacon, crisp cooked and coarsely crumbled

1 scallion, thinly sliced

1 Place the potatoes in a medium saucepan with enough water to cover by 3 inches; bring to a boil. Reduce the heat and simmer until fork-tender, 20–25 minutes. Drain and return to the saucepan.

2 Add the sour cream, milk, salt, and pepper; mash with a potato masher until the potatoes become creamy. Stir in the cheddar. Sprinkle with the bacon and scallion.

In the Kitchen
For a more rustic version of this dish, leave the skins on the potatoes. Make sure you scrub the potatoes well before cooking.

PER SERVING (about ½ cup): 194 Cal, 2 g Fat, 1 g Sat Fat, 0 g Trans Fat, 11 mg Chol, 376 mg Sod, 36 g Carb, 3 g Fib, 9 g Prot, 130 mg Calc. **POINTS** value: **3.**

Try with:
• Home-Style Salisbury Steaks with Mushroom Gravy (page 93)
• Confetti Meatloaf with Cajun Barbecue Sauce (page 123)
• Crispy Oven-Fried Chicken with Sage Gravy (page 133)

BACON-CHEDDAR
MASHED POTATOES

CHILI-SPICED THICK OVEN "FRIES"

PREP 10 MIN • **BAKE** 25 MIN • **SERVES** 4

3 large (8-ounce) russet potatoes, scrubbed

2 teaspoons olive oil

$^1/_2$ teaspoon sugar

$^1/_4$ teaspoon ground cumin

$^1/_4$ teaspoon chili powder

$^1/_4$ teaspoon salt

$^1/_4$ teaspoon black pepper

1 Preheat the oven to 450°F. Spray a large rimmed baking sheet with nonstick spray.

2 Halve the potatoes and cut each piece lengthwise into quarters; place on the baking sheet. Drizzle with the oil and toss to coat. Arrange the potatoes in a single layer and bake until the bottoms are deep golden and crisp, about 15 minutes. Turn the potatoes onto the opposite cut side and bake until crisp, 10–15 minutes longer.

3 Meanwhile, combine the sugar, cumin, chili powder, salt, and pepper in a large bowl. Add the fries and toss to coat.

PER SERVING (6 fries): 151 Cal, 2 g Fat, 0 g Sat Fat, 0 g Trans Fat, 0 mg Chol, 159 mg Sod, 31 g Carb, 4 g Fib, 3 g Prot, 38 mg Calc. **POINTS** value: **2.**

Try with:
• Grilled Spice-Rubbed T-Bone Steak (page 146)
• Open-Face Phillycheese Steak Sandwiches (page 148)
• Cheese-Stuffed Chicken Burgers (page 155)

ROSEMARY ROASTED POTATO SALAD

PREP 15 MIN • **ROAST** 30 MIN • **SERVES** 6

1 1/2 pounds red potatoes, scrubbed and cut into 1-inch pieces

2 teaspoons olive oil

1 teaspoon chopped fresh rosemary

1 medium red bell pepper, thinly sliced

1 medium onion, chopped

1/4 cup fat-free mayonnaise

2 teaspoons balsamic vinegar

1 teaspoon Dijon mustard

1/4 teaspoon salt

1/8 teaspoon black pepper

1 Preheat the oven to 450°F. Spray a large rimmed baking sheet with nonstick spray.

2 Place the potatoes on the baking sheet; add 1 1/2 teaspoons of the oil and the rosemary and toss to coat. Arrange the potatoes in a single layer and roast until the bottoms are deep golden and crisp, about 15 minutes.

3 Meanwhile, toss the bell pepper, onion, and remaining 1/2 teaspoon oil together in a medium bowl. Add to the baking sheet and bake, turning occasionally, until the potatoes are crisp and the pepper and onion are tender, 15–20 minutes longer. Let cool 20 minutes.

▶ **Filling Extra**
Add a green or yellow bell pepper along with the red bell pepper in step 3. This recipe works with the **Simply Filling technique.**

4 Whisk the mayonnaise, vinegar, mustard, salt, and pepper together in a large bowl. Add the potato mixture and toss to coat.

PER SERVING (2/3 cup): 122 Cal, 2 g Fat, 0 g Sat Fat, 0 g Trans Fat, 1 mg Chol, 208 mg Sod, 25 g Carb, 4 g Fib, 2 g Prot, 31 mg Calc. *POINTS* value: *2.*

Try with:
• Tuna Niçoise Sandwiches (page 35)
• California Veggie Sandwiches with Horseradish (page 39)
• Beer-Can Chicken (page 129)

PARMESAN CREAMED SPINACH

PREP 5 MIN • **COOK** 10 MIN • **SERVES** 4

2 (9-ounce) bags baby spinach
$^2/_3$ cup low-fat (1%) milk
1 tablespoon all-purpose flour
1 garlic clove, minced

$^1/_8$ teaspoon ground nutmeg
$^1/_8$ teaspoon black pepper
$^1/_4$ cup grated Parmesan

1 Put the spinach in a steamer basket; set in a large pot over 1 inch of boiling water (the leaves will be tightly packed but will reduce in volume as they wilt). Cover tightly and steam until bright green, about 2 minutes. Drain in a colander; when the spinach is cool enough to handle, squeeze out the excess moisture.

2 Whisk the milk, flour, garlic, nutmeg, and pepper together in a medium saucepan until blended. Bring to a simmer over medium heat, whisking constantly; cook until slightly thickened, about 2 minutes. Whisk in the Parmesan. Add the spinach and cook, stirring constantly, just until heated through, about 2 minutes.

PER SERVING ($^1/_2$ cup): 83 Cal, 3 g Fat, 2 g Sat Fat, 0 g Trans Fat, 7 mg Chol, 232 mg Sod, 9 g Carb, 3 g Fib, 8 g Prot, 261 mg Calc. **POINTS** value: **1.**

Try with:
• Braised Lamb Shanks with Gremolata (page 126)
• Rosemary Roasted Chicken (page 128)
• Grilled Spice-Rubbed T-Bone Steak (page 146)

LEMONY ROASTED BROCCOLI AND CAULIFLOWER

PREP 10 MIN • **ROAST** 20 MIN • **SERVES** 4

4   cups cauliflower florets
4   cups broccoli florets
4   teaspoons extra-virgin olive oil
$\frac{1}{2}$ teaspoon ground cumin

$\frac{1}{4}$ teaspoon salt
$\frac{1}{8}$ teaspoon black pepper
2   teaspoons grated fresh lemon zest

1 Preheat the oven to 425°F. Spray a large rimmed baking sheet with nonstick spray. Place the cauliflower and broccoli on the baking sheet; add the oil, cumin, salt, and pepper, and toss to coat. Spread the vegetables evenly in the pan.

2 Roast, stirring once, until the vegetables are browned and tender, 20–25 minutes.

3 Transfer the vegetables to a medium bowl; add the lemon zest and toss to combine.

In the Kitchen
Substitute grated orange zest for the lemon zest to add a different bright and refreshing citrus flavor to this dish. This recipe works with the **Simply Filling technique.**

PER SERVING (generous 1 cup): 90 Cal, 5 g Fat, 1 g Sat Fat, 0 g Trans Fat, 0 mg Chol, 201 mg Sod, 10 g Carb, 5 g Fib, 4 g Prot, 59 mg Calc. **POINTS** value: **1.**

Try with:
• Smothered Pork Chops with Onion Gravy (page 90)
• Saucy Chicken Marsala (page 96)
• Skillet Macaroni and Cheese (page 108)

EDAMAME-AND-CORN SUCCOTASH WITH BACON

PREP 15 MIN • COOK 15 MIN • SERVES 4

1   cup frozen shelled edamame (green soybeans)
1/2 pound green beans, trimmed and cut into
    2-inch pieces
3   slices center-cut bacon, chopped
1   onion, chopped
2   garlic cloves, minced

1/4 teaspoon dried thyme
1 1/2 cups thawed frozen corn kernels
1   tablespoon light butter
1/4 teaspoon salt
1/8 teaspoon black pepper

1 Bring a large saucepan of lightly salted water to a boil. Add the edamame; return to a boil and cook 4 minutes. Add the green beans, return to a boil, and cook 2 minutes longer or until just crisp-tender. Drain.

2 Meanwhile, cook the bacon in a large nonstick skillet over medium-high heat, stirring occasionally, until the bacon is crisp, 5–6 minutes. With a slotted spoon, transfer the bacon to paper towels to drain.

> **Filling Extra**
> To add more color and nutrients to this side dish, cook 1 red or green bell pepper, diced, along with the onion, garlic, and thyme in step 3.

3 Add the onion, garlic, and thyme to the skillet and cook, stirring often, until the onion begins to soften, 2–3 minutes. Add the corn and cook until crisp-tender, about 3 minutes. Stir in the edamame and green beans and cook until heated through, 2–3 minutes. Stir in the bacon and cook 1 minute longer. Remove from the heat and stir in the butter, salt, and pepper.

PER SERVING (3/4 cup): 156 Cal, 5 g Fat, 2 g Sat Fat, 0 g Trans Fat, 13 mg Chol, 415 mg Sod, 21 g Carb, 5 g Fib, 10 g Prot, 52 mg Calc. *POINTS* value: *3.*

Try with:
• Confetti Meatloaf with Cajun Barbecue Sauce (page 123)
• Beer-Can Chicken (page 129)
• Oven-Barbecued Chicken with Mop Sauce (page 130)

CRISPY SWEET ONION RINGS

PREP 15 MIN • **BAKE** 15 MIN • **SERVES** 4

2 tablespoons all-purpose flour
1/2 teaspoon salt
1/2 teaspoon paprika
1/4 teaspoon black pepper
1/8 teaspoon cayenne

3/4 cup plain dried bread crumbs
2 egg whites, lightly beaten
2 (1/2 pound each) sweet onions, cut crosswise into 1/2-inch slices and separated into 32 rings

1 Preheat the oven to 400°F. Spray two large rimmed baking sheets with nonstick spray.

2 Place the flour, salt, paprika, pepper, and cayenne in a large zip-close plastic bag. Place the bread crumbs in a shallow dish. Place the egg whites in another shallow dish.

3 Place the onion rings, a few at a time, in the flour mixture and shake to coat. Dip each ring into the egg whites, then coat lightly with the bread crumbs. Arrange the rings in a single layer on the baking sheets (reserving for another use any broken or small inner rings) and lightly spray the tops with nonstick spray. Discard the excess flour mixture, egg white, and bread crumbs.

4 Bake until the bottoms of the onion rings are browned, about 10 minutes. Turn the rings and bake until browned, about 5 minutes.

PER SERVING (8 onion rings): 154 Cal, 2 g Fat, 0 g Sat Fat, 0 g Trans Fat, 0 mg Chol, 475 mg Sod, 27 g Carb, 3 g Fib, 6 g Prot, 64 mg Calc. *POINTS* value: *3.*

Try with:
• Fast French Dip Sandwiches (page 150)
• Horseradish Hamburgers (page 153)
• Tuna Melts with Spinach and Jarlsberg (page 160)

GRILLED SPICE-RUBBED
T-BONE STEAK, PAGE 146,

GREEN BEANS WITH LEMON
BROWNED BUTTER, PAGE 180,

GRILLED CORN WITH
CHIPOTLE-LIME BUTTER

GRILLED CORN WITH CHIPOTLE-LIME BUTTER

PREP 10 MIN • **COOK** 15 MIN • **SERVES** 4

4   ears corn-on-the-cob (husks still on)
2   tablespoons light butter, softened
2   teaspoons chopped fresh cilantro

1   teaspoon grated lime zest
¹/₄ teaspoon salt
¹/₈ teaspoon chipotle chile powder

1 Spray the grill rack with nonstick spray. Preheat the grill to medium-high or prepare a medium-high fire.

2 Soak the corn in cold water for 10 minutes. Remove the corn from the water and pull back the husks; remove the silks. Pull the corn husks back over the kernels, twisting the ends to secure the husks.

In the Kitchen
If you aren't a fan of spicy food but enjoy smoky flavors, substitute ¹/₄ teaspoon smoked paprika for the chipotle chile powder.

3 Place the corn on the grill rack and grill, turning every 2 minutes, until black grill marks appear all over the husks, 15–17 minutes.

4 Meanwhile, stir the butter, cilantro, lime zest, salt, and chile powder together in a small bowl. Remove and discard the husks from the corn and serve the corn with the butter.

PER SERVING (1 ear of corn with about 1¹/₂ teaspoons butter mixture): 136 Cal, 4 g Fat, 2 g Sat Fat, 0 g Trans Fat, 7 mg Chol, 183 mg Sod, 26 g Carb, 4 g Fib, 3 g Prot, 5 mg Calc. **POINTS** value: **2.**

Try with:
• Grilled Spice-Rubbed T-Bone Steak (page 146)
• Spicy Chicken Kebabs with Onions, Mushrooms, and Peppers (page 151)
• Jerk Chicken Thighs with Fresh Pineapple Salsa (page 154)

GREEN BEANS WITH LEMON BROWNED BUTTER

PREP 10 MIN • **COOK** 15 MIN • **SERVES** 4

1 **pound green beans, trimmed**
5 **teaspoons unsalted butter**
1½ **teaspoons lemon juice**

½ **teaspoon salt**
⅛ **teaspoon black pepper**

1 Bring a large saucepan of lightly salted water to a boil. Add the beans; return to a boil and cook until just crisp-tender, 2 minutes. Drain.

2 Melt the butter in a large nonstick skillet over medium-high heat; cook until the butter just turns light golden brown, about 2 minutes. Add the beans, lemon juice, salt, and pepper; cook, stirring often, until well coated and heated through, 1–2 minutes.

In the Kitchen
Browning butter gives it a nutty flavor that pairs well with vegetables and fish.

PER SERVING (¾ cup): 74 Cal, 5 g Fat, 3 g Sat Fat, 0 g Trans Fat, 13 mg Chol, 302 mg Sod, 7 g Carb, 3 g Fib, 2 g Prot, 39 mg Calc. *POINTS* value: *1.*

Try with:
• Spicy Shrimp and Rice (page 82)
• Salmon Cakes with Red Pepper Chutney (page 105)
• Autumn Pot Roast with Horseradish Sauce (page 118)

SKILLET-ROASTED BRUSSELS SPROUTS

PREP 15 MIN • **COOK** 15 MIN • **SERVES** 4

2 teaspoons extra-virgin olive oil
1 pound Brussels sprouts, trimmed and quartered
1 cup water
1 medium onion, chopped

3 garlic cloves, sliced
1 tablespoon grated Parmesan
$^1/_4$ teaspoon salt
$^1/_8$ teaspoon black pepper

1 Heat the oil in a large nonstick skillet over medium-high heat. Add the Brussels sprouts and cook, stirring occasionally, until the Brussels sprouts begin to brown, 3–4 minutes. Add the water, bring to a boil, and cook, stirring occasionally, until the water is almost evaporated, about 5 minutes.

2 Add the onion and garlic and cook, stirring occasionally, until the onion is tender and lightly browned, 5–6 minutes. Remove from the heat and stir in the Parmesan, salt, and pepper.

PER SERVING ($^3/_4$ cup): 81 Cal, 3 g Fat, 1 g Sat Fat, 0 g Trans Fat, 1 mg Chol, 203 mg Sod, 11 g Carb, 3 g Fib, 4 g Prot, 73 mg Calc. **POINTS** value: **1.**

Try with:
• Rosemary-Mustard-Crusted Beef Roast (page 120)
• Roast Pork with Gingersnap Gravy (page 125)
• Baked Striped Bass with Bacon Bread Crumbs (page 135)

BALSAMIC ROASTED VEGETABLES

PREP 15 MIN • **BAKE** 25 MIN • **SERVES** 4

1   tablespoon balsamic vinegar

1   tablespoon olive oil

2   teaspoons Dijon mustard

$^1/_4$ teaspoon salt

$^1/_8$ teaspoon black pepper

2   red bell peppers, cut into 1-inch pieces

1   large fennel bulb, cut into thin wedges

1   large zucchini, halved lengthwise and cut into $^1/_2$-inch slices

1   medium red onion, cut into 8 wedges

1 Preheat the oven to 450°F. Spray a large rimmed baking sheet with nonstick spray.

2 Stir the vinegar, oil, mustard, salt, and pepper together in a large bowl. Add the bell peppers, fennel, zucchini, and onion; toss well.

3 Spread the vegetables evenly in the pan. Roast, stirring once, until the vegetables are browned and tender, 25–30 minutes.

> ◆ **Filling Extra**
> Add $^1/_2$ pound fresh asparagus, trimmed and cut into 1-inch pieces, along with the other vegetables. This recipe works with the **Simply Filling technique.**

PER SERVING (generous 1 cup): 97 Cal, 4 g Fat, 1 g Sat Fat, 0 g Trans Fat, 0 mg Chol, 253 mg Sod, 14 g Carb, 5 g Fib, 3 g Prot, 54 mg Calc. **POINTS** value: **1.**

Try with:
• Smothered Pork Chops with Onion Gravy (page 90)
• Saucy Chicken Marsala (page 96)
• Grilled Spice-Rubbed T-Bone Steak (page 146)

STEAKHOUSE CHOPPED SALAD WITH BLUE CHEESE DRESSING

1/4 cup crumbled blue cheese

3 tablespoons reduced-fat mayonnaise

3 tablespoons fat-free sour cream

1 tablespoon apple-cider vinegar

1/2 teaspoon Worcestershire sauce

1/8 teaspoon black pepper

1/2 medium head iceberg lettuce, chopped (about 4 cups)

2 stalks celery, chopped

1 small cucumber, peeled, seeded, and chopped

1 small red onion, chopped

1 small red bell pepper, chopped

1 medium tomato, seeded and chopped

Stir the blue cheese, mayonnaise, sour cream, vinegar, Worcestershire sauce, and pepper together in a large bowl until well mixed. Add the lettuce, celery, cucumber, onion, bell pepper, and tomato; toss well.

> **Filling Extra**
> Add 2 cups chopped romaine lettuce to the salad for more color and crunch.

PER SERVING (1³/4 cups): 95 Cal, 4 g Fat, 2 g Sat Fat, 0 g Trans Fat, 7 mg Chol, 261 mg Sod, 11 g Carb, 3 g Fib, 4 g Prot, 94 mg Calc. *POINTS* value: *2.*

Try with:
- Fettuccine with Fire-Roasted Bolognese Sauce (page 92)
- Family-Style Spaghetti and Chicken Meatballs (page 104)
- Pizza with Sun-Dried-Tomato Sausage and Peppers (page 158)

GRAPE TOMATO–BREAD SALAD

PREP 15 MIN • COOK NONE • SERVES 4

1¹/₂ tablespoons red-wine vinegar

1   tablespoon extra-virgin olive oil

¹/₄ teaspoon salt

¹/₄ teaspoon black pepper

1   (4-ounce) day-old multigrain baguette, cut into ¹/₂-inch cubes

2   cups grape tomatoes, halved

1   medium cucumber, peeled and thinly sliced

1   small red onion, thinly sliced

¹/₄ cup fresh basil leaves, thinly sliced

Whisk the vinegar, oil, salt, and pepper together in a large bowl. Add the bread, tomatoes, cucumber, onion, and basil; toss well. Let the salad stand 15 minutes, tossing occasionally.

> **Filling Extra**
> Bulk up this salad by tossing in 4 cups of mixed baby greens just before serving.

PER SERVING (1¹/₂ cups): 131 Cal, 5 g Fat, 1 g Sat Fat, 0 g Trans Fat, 0 mg Chol, 288 mg Sod, 18 g Carb, 4 g Fib, 5 g Prot, 56 mg Calc. *POINTS* value: *2.*

Try with:
• White Bean-and-Sausage Soup with Escarole (page 41)
• Classic San Francisco–Style Cioppino (page 86)
• Rosemary Roasted Chicken (page 128)

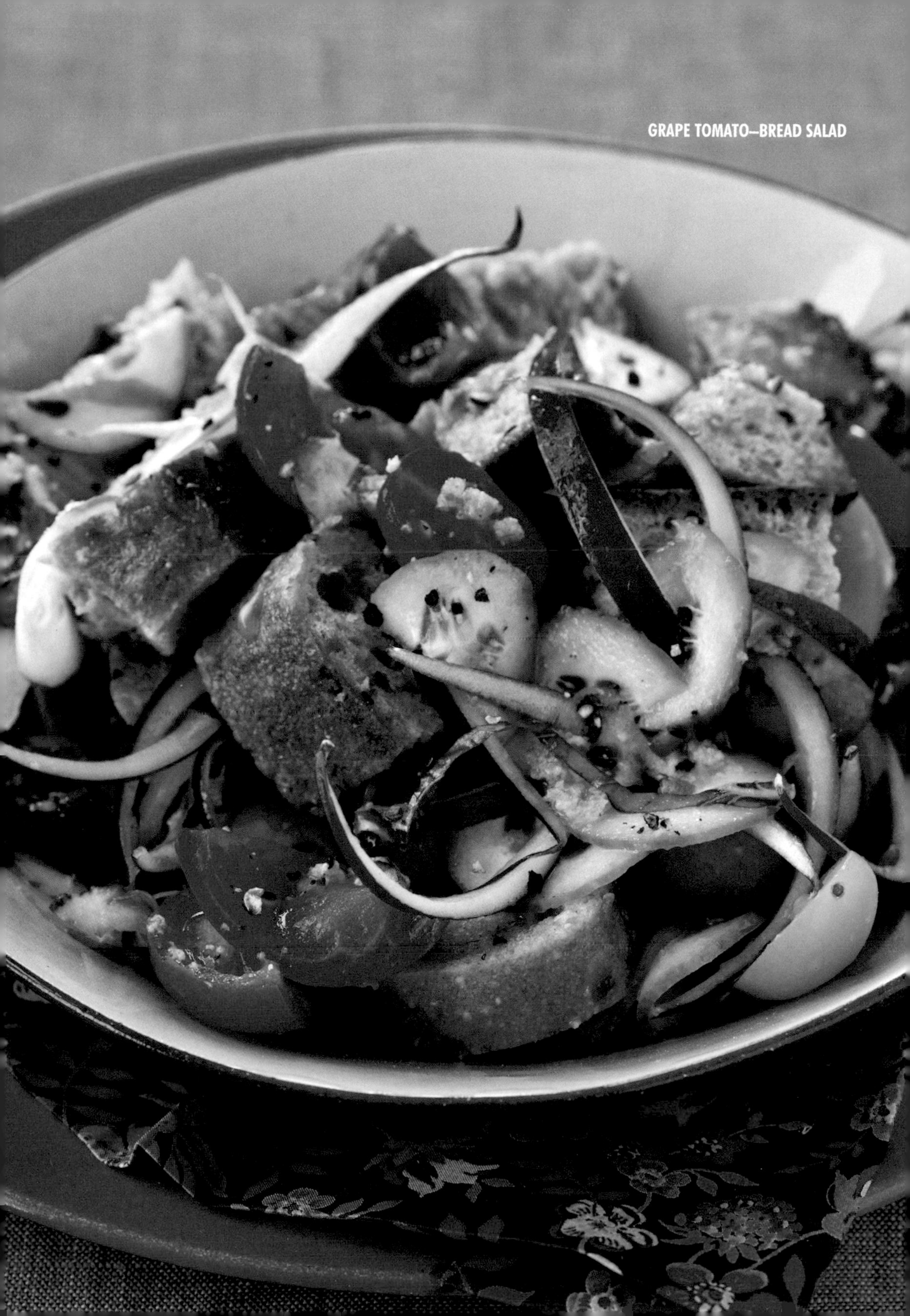
GRAPE TOMATO–BREAD SALAD

APPLE-CARROT SLAW

$^1/_2$ cup reduced-fat mayonnaise

2 tablespoons apple-cider vinegar

2 tablespoons sugar

$^1/_2$ medium head red cabbage, shredded

2 cups shredded carrots

2 medium Granny Smith apples, cored and cut into matchstick strips

$^1/_3$ cup golden raisins

Stir the mayonnaise, vinegar, and sugar together in a large bowl until well mixed. Stir in the cabbage, carrots, apples, and raisins. Let stand 15 minutes before serving. Serve at once or cover with plastic wrap and refrigerate until ready to serve, up to 2 hours.

> **Filling Extra**
> Add 1 small firm-ripe pear, cored and cut into matchstick strips to the slaw.

PER SERVING ($^2/_3$ cup): 144 Cal, 3 g Fat, 0 g Sat Fat, 0 g Trans Fat, 0 mg Chol, 213 mg Sod, 30 g Carb, 4 g Fib, 2 g Prot, 52 mg Calc. **POINTS** value: **2.**

Try with:
- New Orleans Muffaletta Sandwich (page 36)
- Pulled Chicken Sandwiches (page 103)
- Crispy Unfried Fish and Chips (page 138)

PASTA SALAD WITH TOMATOES AND MOZZARELLA

PREP 10 MIN • **COOK** 20 MIN • **SERVES** 6

6 ounces whole wheat penne

2 teaspoons olive oil

2 garlic cloves, minced

1/4 teaspoon crushed red pepper

2 teaspoons lemon zest

2 tablespoons lemon juice

1/2 teaspoon salt

1/4 teaspoon black pepper

2 ounces fresh mozzarella cheese, diced

1 cup cherry tomatoes, halved

1/2 cup chopped fresh basil

1 Cook the penne according to the package directions, omitting the salt if desired. Drain and rinse under cold running water. Drain again.

2 To make the dressing, heat the oil in a small skillet over medium heat. Add the garlic and red pepper and cook, stirring often, until the garlic is golden, 2–3 minutes. Transfer the oil mixture to a large bowl; stir in the lemon zest, lemon juice, salt, and pepper. Add the pasta, mozzarella, tomatoes, and basil; toss to coat.

In the Kitchen
Lightly toasting the garlic adds a nutty flavor to the dressing. Watch it carefully as it cooks; if it browns too much it will have a bitter flavor.

PER SERVING (about 3/4 cup): 142 Cal, 4 g Fat, 1 g Sat Fat, 0 g Trans Fat, 3 mg Chol, 207 mg Sod, 19 g Carb, 4 g Fib, 7 g Prot, 12 mg Calc. **POINTS** value: **2.**

Try with:
- Smoked Turkey, Cheese, and Apple Wraps (page 34)
- California Veggie Sandwiches with Horseradish (page 39)
- Rosemary Roasted Chicken (page 128)

Down-Home
DESSERTS

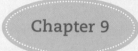

Chapter 9

Lemon-Ginger Bundt Cake

PREP 20 MIN • BAKE 45 MIN • SERVES 20

CAKE

2 tablespoons + 1¼ cups granulated sugar
2½ cups all-purpose flour
2 teaspoons baking powder
½ teaspoon baking soda
½ teaspoon salt
1 cup low-fat buttermilk
⅓ cup canola oil
1 tablespoon grated lemon zest
2 tablespoons lemon juice

1 tablespoon minced peeled fresh ginger
2 large eggs
1 large egg white

GLAZE

1 cup confectioners' sugar
2 tablespoons low-fat buttermilk
1 tablespoon grated lemon zest
1 tablespoon lemon juice

1 To make the cake, preheat the oven to 350°F. Spray a 10-inch Bundt pan with nonstick spray. Sprinkle the bottom and sides of the pan with 2 tablespoons of the granulated sugar.

2 Whisk the remaining 1¼ cups granulated sugar, flour, baking powder, baking soda, and salt together in a large bowl. Whisk the buttermilk, oil, lemon zest, lemon juice, ginger, eggs, and egg white together in a medium bowl. Add the buttermilk mixture to the flour mixture, stirring just until blended.

3 Pour the batter into the pan. Bake until golden brown and a toothpick inserted into the center comes out clean, 45–50 minutes. Let cool in the pan on a rack 10 minutes. Remove the cake from the pan and let cool completely on the rack.

4 To make the glaze, whisk the confectioners' sugar, buttermilk, lemon zest, and lemon juice together in a small bowl until smooth. Place the cake on a serving plate. Pour the glaze over, allowing it to drip down the side of the cake. Let stand until set, about 10 minutes.

PER SERVING (¹⁄₂₀ of cake): 181 Cal, 4 g Fat, 1 g Sat Fat, 0 g Trans Fat, 22 mg Chol, 222 mg Sod, 33 g Carb, 1 g Fib, 3 g Prot, 50 mg Calc. *POINTS* value: *4.*

CHOCOLATE ANGEL FOOD CAKE WITH ESPRESSO GLAZE

PREP 25 MIN • **BAKE** 35 MIN • **SERVES** 12

CAKE
1¹/₂ cups cake flour
¹/₂ cup unsweetened cocoa powder
¹/₂ teaspoon salt
12 large egg whites, at room temperature
1 teaspoon cream of tartar
1¹/₂ cups granulated sugar
1 teaspoon vanilla extract

GLAZE
1 tablespoon hot water
1 teaspoon instant espresso powder
²/₃ cup confectioners' sugar
1 teaspoon vanilla extract

1 To make the cake, place an oven rack in the lower third of the oven and preheat the oven to 375°F.

2 Sift together the flour, cocoa, and salt into a medium bowl. With an electric mixer on medium speed, beat the egg whites and cream of tartar until soft peaks form. Add the sugar, 2 tablespoons at a time, beating until stiff, glossy peaks form. Beat in the vanilla.

3 Sift the flour mixture, one-third at a time, over the beaten egg whites, gently folding it in with a rubber spatula just until the cocoa is no longer visible. (Be careful not to overmix.)

4 Scrape the batter into an ungreased 10-inch tube pan; spread evenly. Bake until the cake springs back when lightly pressed, 35–40 minutes. Invert the pan onto its legs or the neck of a bottle and let cool completely. Run a thin knife around the edge of the cake to loosen it from the side and center tube of the pan. Place the cake on a serving plate.

In the Kitchen
Egg whites beat to a larger volume, making a taller cake, when at room temperature. To warm the eggs quickly, place them in a bowl of warm water for 15 minutes.

5 To make the glaze, whisk the water and espresso powder together in a small bowl until the espresso is dissolved. Whisk in the confectioners' sugar and the vanilla until smooth. Pour the glaze over, allowing it to drip down the side of the cake. Let stand until set, about 10 minutes.

PER SERVING (¹/₁₂ of cake): 212 Cal, 1 g Fat, 0 g Sat Fat, 0 g Trans Fat, 0 mg Chol, 155 mg Sod, 48 g Carb, 1 g Fib, 6 g Prot, 10 mg Calc. **POINTS** value: **4.**

CHOCOLATE-STUDDED CANNOLI CAKE

PREP 20 MIN • **BAKE** 35 MIN • **SERVES** 20

CAKE

2   cups cake flour

2   teaspoons baking powder

¹/₂ teaspoon baking soda

¹/₂ teaspoon salt

2   large eggs, at room temperature

2   large egg whites, at room temperature

¹/₂ cup granulated sugar

¹/₂ cup low-fat buttermilk

¹/₄ cup canola oil

¹/₂ cup mini semisweet chocolate chips

FROSTING

1   (15-ounce) container fat-free ricotta

1   (3-ounce) package fat-free cream cheese, at room temperature

³/₄ cup confectioners' sugar

1   tablespoon grated orange zest

1   teaspoon vanilla extract

1   tablespoon chopped unsalted pistachio nuts

1 To make the cake, preheat the oven to 350°F. Spray two 8-inch round cake pans with nonstick spray; line with wax-paper rounds and spray with nonstick spray.

2 Whisk the flour, baking powder, baking soda, and salt together in a medium bowl. With an electric mixer on high speed, beat the eggs and egg whites in a large bowl until thickened, about 2 minutes. Gradually add the granulated sugar, beating until light and fluffy, about 3 minutes. On low speed, add the buttermilk and oil, beating just until blended. Add the flour mixture, beating just until incorporated. Stir in the chocolate chips.

3 Spoon the batter into the pans. Bake until a toothpick inserted into the centers comes out clean, about 35 minutes. Let cool in the pans on racks 10 minutes. Invert the layers onto racks. Peel off the wax paper and let cool completely on the racks.

4 To make the frosting, with an electric mixer at high speed, beat the ricotta, cream cheese, confectioners' sugar, orange zest, and vanilla in a medium bowl until smooth, about 1 minute.

5 Place 1 cake layer, rounded side down, on a serving plate. With a narrow metal spatula, spread ¹/₂ cup of the frosting over the layer. Top with the remaining layer, rounded side up. Spread the remaining frosting over the top and side of the cake. Sprinkle the pistachios on top of the cake.

PER SERVING (¹/₂₀ of cake): 170 Cal, 5 g Fat, 1 g Sat Fat, 0 g Trans Fat, 24 mg Chol, 199 mg Sod, 25 g Carb, 1 g Fib, 6 g Prot, 88 mg Calc. *POINTS* value: *4.*

CHOCOLATE-STUDDED
CANNOLI CAKE

WARM GINGERBREAD CAKE WITH LEMON SAUCE

PREP 20 MIN • BAKE/COOK 30 MIN • SERVES 16

CAKE
- 2 cups all-purpose flour
- 1 teaspoon baking powder
- 1 teaspoon cinnamon
- $1/2$ teaspoon ground ginger
- $1/2$ teaspoon ground allspice
- $1/2$ teaspoon salt
- $1/2$ cup unsulphured molasses
- $1/2$ cup packed light brown sugar
- $1/4$ cup canola oil
- 1 large egg
- $1/2$ cup hot water

SAUCE
- $3/4$ cup water
- 3 tablespoons granulated sugar
- 3 tablespoons lemon juice
- 2 teaspoons cornstarch
- 2 teaspoons grated lemon zest
- 1 teaspoon light butter

1 To make the cake, preheat the oven to 350°F. Spray a 9-inch square baking pan with nonstick spray.

2 Whisk the flour, baking powder, cinnamon, ginger, allspice, and salt together in a large bowl. Whisk the molasses, brown sugar, oil, and egg together in a medium bowl. Whisk the hot water into the molasses mixture until blended. Add the molasses mixture to the flour mixture; stir until well blended.

3 Scrape the batter into the pan. Bake until a toothpick inserted into the center comes out clean, 30–35 minutes. Let cool in the pan on a rack 15 minutes. Remove the cake from the pan and let cool on the rack. Cut into 16 squares.

4 Meanwhile, to make the sauce, combine the water, granulated sugar, lemon juice, and cornstarch in a medium saucepan and set over medium heat. Bring to a boil, whisking, until thickened and bubbly, 1–2 minutes. Remove from the heat and stir in the lemon zest and butter. Serve the cake and the sauce warm or at room temperature.

PER SERVING ($1/16$ of cake with 1 tablespoon sauce): 161 Cal, 4 g Fat, 0 g Sat Fat, 0 g Trans Fat, 14 mg Chol, 135 mg Sod, 30 g Carb, 1 g Fib, 2 g Prot, 52 mg Calc. **POINTS** value: **3.**

GOLDEN ZUCCHINI-APPLE LOAF CAKE

PREP 25 MIN • BAKE 1 HR 10 MIN • SERVES 16

1¹/₂ cups all-purpose flour
¹/₂ cup whole-wheat flour
³/₄ cup sugar
2 teaspoons cinnamon
2 teaspoons baking powder
¹/₂ teaspoon baking soda
¹/₂ teaspoon salt

1 cup unsweetened applesauce
³/₄ cup fat-free Greek yogurt
¹/₃ cup canola oil
2 large eggs
1 large egg white
1 teaspoon vanilla extract
2 cups shredded zucchini

1 Preheat the oven to 350°F. Spray a 5 x 9-inch loaf pan with nonstick spray.

2 Whisk the flours, sugar, cinnamon, baking powder, baking soda, and salt together in a large bowl. Whisk the applesauce, yogurt, oil, eggs, egg white, and vanilla together in a medium bowl. Add the yogurt mixture to the flour mixture; stir just until the flour mixture is moistened. Stir in the zucchini just until combined.

In the Kitchen
You can store this cake in the refrigerator for up to 1 week. Warm a slice in the toaster oven or microwave for a few seconds before serving.

3 Scrape the batter into the pan. Bake until a toothpick inserted into the center of the cake comes out clean, 1 hour and 10 minutes. Let cool in the pan on a rack 10 minutes. Remove the cake from the pan and let cool completely on the rack.

PER SERVING (¹/₁₆ of cake): 160 Cal, 5 g Fat, 1 g Sat Fat, 0 g Trans Fat, 27 mg Chol, 197 mg Sod, 25 g Carb, 1 g Fib, 4 g Prot, 71 mg Calc. *POINTS* value: *3.*

RED VELVET CAKE WITH
CREAM CHEESE FROSTING

RED VELVET CAKE WITH CREAM CHEESE FROSTING

PREP 20 MIN • **BAKE** 35 MIN • **SERVES** 16

CAKE

2	cups cake flour
3	tablespoons unsweetened cocoa powder
2	teaspoons baking powder
$1/2$	teaspoon baking soda
$1/2$	teaspoon salt
$3/4$	cup low-fat buttermilk
$3/4$	cup granulated sugar
3	tablespoons canola oil
1	large egg
1	teaspoon red food coloring

FROSTING

1	(8-ounce) package fat-free cream cheese, at room temperature
$1^1/4$	cups confectioners' sugar
$1/2$	cup fat-free Greek yogurt
$3/4$	teaspoon vanilla extract
$1/4$	cup chopped pecans

1 To make the cake, preheat the oven to 350°F. Spray an 8-inch round baking pan with nonstick spray.

2 Whisk the flour, baking powder, cocoa, baking soda, and salt together in a large bowl. Whisk the buttermilk, granulated sugar, oil, egg, and food coloring together in a medium bowl. Add the buttermilk mixture to the flour mixture; stir until well blended.

3 Scrape the batter into the pan. Bake until a toothpick inserted into the center comes out clean, 35–40 minutes. Let cool completely in the pan on a rack. Run a knife around the edge of the cake to loosen it from the pan. Invert.

4 To make the frosting, with an electric mixer on high speed, beat the cream cheese, confectioners' sugar, yogurt, and vanilla in a medium bowl until smooth, about 1 minute.

5 Split the cake layer in half with a long serrated knife. Place the bottom layer, cut side up, on a serving plate. Spread $1/2$ cup of the frosting evenly over the layer, leaving a $1/2$-inch border. Place the remaining cake layer on top, rounded side up. Spread the remaining 1 cup frosting over the top and side of the cake. Sprinkle the pecans on the side of the cake, pressing to adhere.

PER SERVING ($1/16$ of cake): 197 Cal, 5 g Fat, 1 g Sat Fat, 0 g Trans Fat, 15 mg Chol, 274 mg Sod, 34 g Carb, 0 g Fib, 5 g Prot, 95 mg Calc. *POINTS* value: *4.*

PINEAPPLE-GINGER UPSIDE-DOWN CUPCAKES

PREP 25 MIN • COOK/BAKE 25 MIN • SERVES 12

1/2 cup packed light brown sugar

1 tablespoon finely chopped crystallized ginger

2 teaspoons unsalted butter

1 (20-ounce) can pineapple chunks, drained

1 1/4 cups all-purpose flour

1 1/4 teaspoons baking powder

1/4 teaspoon salt

1/2 cup granulated sugar

1/2 cup 1% (low fat) milk

3 tablespoons canola oil

1 large egg

1 teaspoon vanilla extract

1 Preheat the oven to 350°F. Spray a 12-cup muffin pan with nonstick spray.

2 Combine the brown sugar, ginger, and butter in a small saucepan and set over medium heat. Cook, stirring constantly, until the butter melts and the sugar is dissolved, about 3 minutes. Remove from the heat and stir in the pineapple. Spoon the pineapple mixture evenly into the muffin cups.

In the Kitchen
Before chopping crystallized ginger, spray your knife with nonstick spray to keep the ginger from sticking to the blade.

3 Whisk the flour, baking powder, and salt together in a small bowl. Whisk the granulated sugar, milk, oil, egg, and vanilla together in a large bowl. Add the sugar mixture to the flour mixture and stir just until blended.

4 Fill the muffin cups evenly with the batter. Bake until a toothpick inserted into the center comes out clean, about 20 minutes. Let cool in the pan on a rack 10 minutes. To loosen, run a thin knife around the side of the muffin cups. Remove the cupcakes from the pan and cool upside down on the rack. If necessary, cut a thin slice off the tops of the muffins so they stand upright. Drizzle any extra syrup from the muffin pan over the cupcakes

PER SERVING (1 cupcake): 190 Cal, 5 g Fat, 1 g Sat Fat, 0 g Trans Fat, 20 mg Chol, 115 mg Sod, 35 g Carb, 1 g Fib, 2 g Prot, 55 mg Calc. *POINTS* value: *4.*

STREUSEL-TOPPED APRICOT-SPICE MUFFINS

PREP 15 MIN • BAKE 20 MIN • SERVES 12

TOPPING
1/4 cup all-purpose flour
1/4 cup packed light brown sugar
2 tablespoons light butter, softened
1 teaspoon cinnamon
1/4 teaspoon salt

MUFFINS
1 1/2 cups all-purpose flour
1 1/2 teaspoons baking powder

1 teaspoon cinnamon
1/2 teaspoon baking soda
1/2 teaspoon ground allspice
1/4 teaspoon salt
3/4 cup granulated sugar
1/2 cup fat-free Greek yogurt
1/2 cup apricot fruit spread
1/4 cup fat-free milk
3 tablespoons canola oil
1 large egg

1 Preheat the oven to 375°F. Line a 12-cup muffin pan with paper liners.

2 To make the streusel topping, stir the flour, brown sugar, butter, cinnamon, and salt together in a small bowl. Set aside.

3 To make the muffins, whisk the flour, baking powder, cinnamon, baking soda, allspice, and salt together in a large bowl. Whisk the sugar, yogurt, fruit spread, milk, oil, and egg together in a medium bowl. Add the brown sugar mixture to the flour mixture and stir just until the flour is moistened.

4 Fill the muffin cups evenly with the batter. Sprinkle the streusel evenly on the batter. Bake until a toothpick inserted into the center comes out clean, 20–25 minutes. Cool in the pan on a rack 5 minutes. Remove the muffins from the pan and cool on the rack. Serve warm or at room temperature.

PER SERVING (1 muffin): 217 Cal, 5 g Fat, 1 g Sat Fat, 0 g Trans Fat, 20 mg Chol, 241 mg Sod, 41 g Carb, 2 g Fib, 3 g Prot, 80 mg Calc. **POINTS** value: **4.**

SINFUL CHOCOLATE-CAPPUCCINO MOUSSE PIE

PREP 20 MIN • COOK 5 MIN • SERVES 10

1¼ cups fat-free milk

1 large egg

¼ cup sugar

2 tablespoons instant espresso powder

1 envelope unflavored gelatin

½ teaspoon salt

¼ cup semisweet chocolate chips

1 teaspoon vanilla extract

6 tablespoons warm water

2 tablespoons powdered egg whites

1 cup thawed frozen fat-free whipped topping

1 (6-ounce) prepared chocolate cookie crust

½ ounce semisweet chocolate, coarsely grated

1 To make the filling, whisk the milk, egg, sugar, espresso powder, gelatin, and salt together in a medium saucepan and set over medium-low heat. Cook, stirring constantly, until the sugar and gelatin are completely dissolved, about 3 minutes (do not let boil). Remove from the heat. Add the chocolate chips and vanilla and stir until the chocolate is melted. Pour into a medium bowl; refrigerate until the filling begins to set, about 30 minutes.

2 Stir the warm water and powdered egg whites together in a medium bowl until the egg white powder is completely dissolved, about 2 minutes. With an electric mixer on medium speed, beat the egg white mixture until stiff, glossy peaks form.

> ▸ **Filling Extra**
> Garnish each serving of pie with a handful of fresh strawberries.

3 With a rubber spatula, gently fold the beaten egg whites and whipped topping into the filling until no streaks of white remain. Spoon into the crust; spread evenly. Refrigerate until firm, at least 3 hours and up to 1 day. Just before serving, sprinkle with the chocolate.

PER SERVING (¹/₁₀ of pie): 176 Cal, 7 g Fat, 2 g Sat Fat, 1 g Trans Fat, 22 mg Chol, 262 mg Sod, 25 g Carb, 1 g Fib, 4 g Prot, 43 mg Calc. *POINTS* value: **4.**

FROZEN PEANUT
BUTTER-AND-
CHOCOLATE PIE

FROZEN PEANUT BUTTER-AND-CHOCOLATE PIE

PREP 10 MIN • COOK 5 MIN • SERVES 12

1¹/₂ cups fat-free milk

¹/₄ cup granulated sugar

¹/₂ cup + 1 tablespoon reduced-fat creamy peanut butter

³/₄ teaspoon vanilla extract

¹/₂ cup frozen thawed fat-free whipped topping

1 (6-ounce) prepared reduced-fat graham-cracker crust

1 tablespoon chopped dry roasted peanuts

¹/₂ ounce semisweet chocolate, coarsely grated

1 Combine the milk and sugar in a medium saucepan and set over medium-high heat. Cook, stirring constantly, until the sugar is completely dissolved, about 2 minutes; remove from the heat. Whisk in the peanut butter and vanilla until smooth. Pour into a medium bowl and refrigerate until completely cooled, about 1 hour.

2 Gently stir the whipped topping into the chilled milk mixture; spoon into the crust. Sprinkle with the peanuts and grated chocolate. Loosely cover the pie with wax paper, then with heavy-duty foil. Freeze until completely frozen, at least 4 hours or up to 2 days. Let the pie soften at room temperature 15 minutes before serving.

PER SERVING (¹/₁₂ of pie): 175 Cal, 7 g Fat, 2 g Sat Fat, 1 g Trans Fat, 1 mg Chol, 156 mg Sod, 23 g Carb, 1 g Fib, 5 g Prot, 45 mg Calc. **POINTS** value: **4.**

BERRIES WITH RUM CRÈME ANGLAISE

PREP 15 MIN • **COOK** 10 MIN • **SERVES** 4

1 cup fat-free milk

1 tablespoon light rum or $^1/_2$ teaspoon rum extract

$^1/_2$ teaspoon vanilla extract

2 tablespoons sugar

2 large egg yolks

1 cup sliced strawberries

1 cup blueberries

1 cup raspberries

1 cup blackberries

1 Bring the milk just to a boil in a medium saucepan set over medium heat. Remove from the heat and stir in the rum and vanilla.

2 Meanwhile, whisk the sugar and yolks together in a medium bowl. Slowly add $^1/_2$ cup of the hot milk mixture, whisking constantly. Slowly pour the egg mixture back into the hot milk mixture, whisking constantly. Cook over low heat, whisking constantly, until the custard thickens and coats the back of a spoon, about 5 minutes. (Do not let boil.)

In the Kitchen
Crème anglaise is a light custard sauce that goes well with any fresh fruit. Try it drizzled over toasted slices of fat-free pound cake or angel food cake.

3 Immediately pour the custard into a bowl and let cool to room temperature. Cover and refrigerate until chilled, at least 2 hours or up to 1 day.

4 Place the berries in a large bowl and toss gently to combine. Spoon 1 cup of the berries into each of 4 goblets or dessert dishes and spoon about $^1/_4$ cup of the custard over the berries.

PER SERVING (1 cup berries with $^1/_4$ cup custard): 147 Cal, 3 g Fat, 1 g Sat Fat, 0 g Trans Fat, 104 mg Chol, 31 mg Sod, 25 g Carb, 6 g Fib, 5 g Prot, 114 mg Calc. **POINTS** value: **2.**

RASPBERRY-CHERRY CLAFOUTI

PREP 10 MIN • BAKE 30 MIN • SERVES 6

2   cups fresh raspberries
1   (10-ounce) bag thawed frozen pitted cherries
2   tablespoons kirsch
1/2 cup fat-free milk
1/3 cup granulated sugar

3   tablespoons all-purpose flour
2   large eggs
1   tablespoon minced peeled fresh ginger
1   tablespoon melted butter
1   tablespoon confectioners' sugar

1 Preheat the oven to 375°F. Spray a 9-inch pie plate with nonstick spray.

2 Combine the raspberries, cherries, and kirsch in a large bowl and toss gently to coat. Spoon the raspberry mixture into the baking dish.

3 Combine the milk, sugar, flour, eggs, ginger, and butter in a food processor. Process until smooth and pour over the raspberry mixture.

4 Bake until a toothpick inserted near the center comes out clean, 30–35 minutes. Let cool about 15 minutes to serve warm, or serve at room temperature. Sprinkle with the confectioners' sugar just before serving.

PER SERVING (1/6 of clafouti): 179 Cal, 4 g Fat, 2 g Sat Fat, 0 g Trans Fat, 76 mg Chol, 44 mg Sod, 31 g Carb, 4 g Fib, 4 g Prot, 52 mg Calc. **POINTS** value: **3.**

Ambrosia Trifle

PREP 20 MIN • COOK NONE • SERVES 6

1 (1-ounce) package reduced-calorie vanilla-flavored instant pudding mix

1³/₄ cups fat-free milk

5 cups (2-inch) cubes angel food cake

¹/₂ cup orange juice

1 (20-ounce) can pineapple chunks, drained

2 navel oranges, peeled and cut into sections

1 (6-ounce) container fresh raspberries

¹/₄ cup thawed frozen fat-free whipped topping

2 tablespoons shredded sweetened coconut, toasted

1 Whisk the pudding mix and milk together in a large bowl until thickened, about 2 minutes.

2 Line the bottom of a medium glass bowl with half of the cake cubes. Drizzle with half of the orange juice. Top with half of the pudding, half of the pineapple, half of the oranges, and half of the raspberries. Repeat the layering once.

3 Refrigerate, covered, until thoroughly chilled, at least 3 hours or up to 8 hours. Top with dollops of the whipped topping and sprinkle with the coconut just before serving.

PER SERVING (1 cup): 250 Cal, 1 g Fat, 1 g Sat Fat, 0 g Trans Fat, 1 mg Chol, 527 mg Sod, 56 g Carb, 4 g Fib, 6 g Prot, 137 mg Calc. **POINTS** value: **4.**

Rosy Strawberry Rice Pudding

PREP 10 MIN • COOK 40 MIN • SERVES 6

4   cups fat-free milk
1   cup Arborio rice
1/4 cup + 2 tablespoons sugar

1/2 teaspoon ground cardamom
1 1/2 cups sliced strawberries

1 Bring the milk, rice, 1/4 cup of the sugar, and cardamom to a boil in a medium saucepan. Reduce the heat and simmer, covered, stirring often, until the mixture is thick and creamy and the rice is very soft, about 35 minutes.

2 Meanwhile, heat the strawberries and the remaining 2 tablespoons sugar in a small saucepan, stirring occasionally, until the sugar is dissolved and the strawberries just begin to soften, about 2 minutes.

3 Remove the pudding from the heat and stir in the strawberry mixture. Let stand at room temperature to cool slightly. Serve warm or let cool, cover, and refrigerate until chilled, about 2 hours.

> ♦ **Filling Extra**
> To turn this dessert into a double berry treat, top each serving of the pudding with 1/4 cup fresh raspberries.

PER SERVING (1/2 cup pudding): 241 Cal, 1 g Fat, 0 g Sat Fat, 0 g Trans Fat, 3 mg Chol, 70 mg Sod, 51 g Carb, 1 g Fib, 8 g Prot, 221 mg Calc. *POINTS* value: **5.**

CREAMY COCONUT-RUM BREAD PUDDING

PREP 20 MIN • **BAKE** 30 MIN • **SERVES** 6

1/2 cup dried currants

2 tablespoons coconut-flavored rum

2 cups low-fat (1%) milk

1 cup fat-free half-and-half

1/4 cup sugar

2 large eggs

1 large egg white

1 teaspoon vanilla extract

1 teaspoon cinnamon

1/4 teaspoon ground nutmeg

4 cups 1-inch cubes whole grain French bread

1 Preheat the oven to 375°F. Spray a 7 x 11-inch baking dish with nonstick spray.

2 Combine the currants and rum in a small bowl. Let stand 10 minutes.

3 Meanwhile, whisk the milk, half-and-half, sugar, eggs, egg white, vanilla, cinnamon, and nutmeg together in a large bowl. Stir in the bread cubes, pressing down on the cubes so that they soak up the liquid. Let stand 5 minutes, stirring occasionally. Stir in the currant mixture. Pour into the baking dish.

4 Bake, uncovered, until lightly puffed and golden and a knife inserted in the center comes out clean, 30–35 minutes. Let cool about 15 minutes to serve warm, or serve at room temperature.

In the Kitchen
You can substitute 2 tablespoons orange juice, 1/2 teaspoon rum extract, and 1/4 teaspoon coconut extract for the coconut-flavored rum.

PER SERVING (1/6 of bread pudding): 232 Cal, 4 g Fat, 2 g Sat Fat, 0 g Trans Fat, 77 mg Chol, 250 mg Sod, 37 g Carb, 3 g Fib, 10 g Prot, 188 mg Calc. **POINTS** value: **4.**

CREAMY COCONUT-RUM BREAD PUDDING

BEST-EVER MINT CHOCOLATE CHIP ICE CREAM

PREP 10 MIN • COOK NONE • SERVES 10

4   cups fat-free half-and-half

²/₃ cup sugar

1   teaspoon peppermint extract

³/₄ cup mini semisweet chocolate chips

1 Whisk the half-and-half, sugar, and extract in a large bowl until the sugar is dissolved, 2–3 minutes.

2 Pour the mixture into an ice-cream maker and freeze according to the manufacturer's instructions, adding the chocolate chips about 10 minutes before the ice cream is done. Transfer the ice cream to a freezer container and freeze until firm, at least 2 hours or up to 6 hours. This ice cream is best served on the day it's made.

PER SERVING (½ cup): 171 Cal, 5 g Fat, 3 g Sat Fat, 0 g Trans Fat, 5 mg Chol, 141 mg Sod, 30 g Carb, 1 g Fib, 3 g Prot, 97 mg Calc. **POINTS** value: **4.**

Cool-and-Creamy Key Lime Sorbet

PREP 10 MIN • **COOK** 10 MIN • **SERVES** 9

$^3/_4$ **cup water**

$^1/_4$ **cup sugar**

1 **(14-ounce) can fat-free sweetened condensed milk**

$^1/_2$ **cup bottled key lime juice**

1 **tablespoon grated lemon zest**

1 Combine the water and sugar in a small saucepan and set over high heat. Bring to a boil, stirring until the sugar is dissolved. Reduce the heat and simmer 5 minutes. Transfer to a medium bowl and let cool to room temperature. Cover and refrigerate until chilled, about 3 hours.

2 Stir in the condensed milk, lime juice, and lemon zest. Pour the mixture into an 8-inch square baking pan. Cover tightly with foil and freeze until frozen along the edges, about 1 hour. With a fork, scrape the ice at the edges in toward the center. Return to the freezer for 1 hour, then scrape again. Cover and freeze until almost firm, about 45 minutes.

3 Transfer the sorbet to a food processor. Pulse 4–5 times or until the sorbet is smooth (do not overprocess or the sorbet will melt). Scrape into a container with a tight-fitting lid; freeze until firm.

In the Kitchen

You can squeeze regular limes if key lime juice is unavailable. You will need about 4 large limes for the $^1/_2$ cup of juice needed for this recipe.

PER SERVING ($^1/_3$ cup): 196 Cal, 0 g Fat, 0 g Sat Fat, 0 g Trans Fat, 8 mg Chol, 63 mg Sod, 44 g Carb, 0 g Fib, 5 g Prot, 158 mg Calc. *POINTS* value: **4.**

SINFUL CHOCOLATE-CAPPUCCINO
MOUSSE PIE, PAGE 201, AND
ROCKY ROAD BROWNIES

ROCKY ROAD BROWNIES

PREP 15 MIN • BAKE 20 MIN • SERVES 16

1 cup all-purpose flour
1/2 cup unsweetened cocoa powder
1 teaspoon baking powder
1/4 teaspoon salt
3/4 cup sugar
1/2 cup apple butter

1/4 cup canola oil
2 large eggs
2 teaspoons vanilla extract
1/2 cup mini-marshmallows
1/4 cup semisweet chocolate chips
1/4 cup chopped walnuts

1 Preheat the oven to 350°F. Line an 8-inch square baking pan with foil, allowing the foil to extend over the rim of the pan by 2 inches. Spray with nonstick spray.

2 Whisk the flour, cocoa, baking powder, and salt together in a large bowl. Whisk the sugar, apple butter, oil, eggs and vanilla together in a medium bowl. Add the sugar mixture to the flour mixture; stir just until blended.

3 Scrape the batter into the baking pan and spread evenly. Sprinkle with the marshmallows, chocolate chips, and walnuts. Bake until a toothpick inserted into the center comes out with moist crumbs clinging, 20–25 minutes. Let cool completely in the pan on a rack. Lift from the pan using the foil as handles; cut into 16 squares.

PER SERVING (1 square): 159 Cal, 7 g Fat, 1 g Sat Fat, 0 g Trans Fat, 27 mg Chol, 78 mg Sod, 25 g Carb, 2 g Fib, 3 g Prot, 29 mg Calc. *POINTS* value: *3.*

FAVORITE OATMEAL-RAISIN COOKIES

PREP 15 MIN • **BAKE** 12 MIN • **MAKES** 32

1¹/₂ cup quick-cooking (not instant) oats

³/₄ cup whole-wheat flour

1 teaspoon cinnamon

¹/₂ teaspoon baking soda

¹/₄ teaspoon salt

¹/₂ cup granulated sugar

¹/₄ cup packed light brown sugar

4 tablespoons unsalted butter, softened

1 tablespoon canola oil

1 large egg

1 teaspoon vanilla extract

¹/₂ cup raisins

¹/₄ cup chopped walnuts

1 Preheat the oven to 350°F. Spray 2 large baking sheets with nonstick spray.

2 Combine the oats, flour, cinnamon, baking soda, and salt in a medium bowl. With an electric mixer on medium speed, beat the sugars, butter, and oil in a large bowl until creamy. Beat in the egg and vanilla just until blended. Add the flour mixture and beat just until blended. Stir in the raisins and walnuts.

3 Drop the dough by level measuring tablespoons, about 1 inch apart, onto the baking sheets, making a total of 32 cookies. With your fingers, lightly press each mound to make 2-inch rounds. Bake until the cookies are lightly browned, 12–15 minutes, rotating the baking sheets halfway through the baking. Let cool on the baking sheets on racks 1 minute. With a spatula, transfer the cookies to racks and let cool completely.

In the Kitchen
You can substitute dried cranberries for the raisins, and almonds or pecans for the walnuts in this recipe.

PER SERVING (1 cookie): 75 Cal, 3 g Fat, 1 g Sat Fat, 0 g Trans Fat, 10 mg Chol, 41 mg Sod, 11 g Carb, 1 g Fib, 1 g Prot, 8 mg Calc. *POINTS* value: *2.*

PRETTY-IN-PINK LEMONADE COOKIES

PREP 20 MIN • BAKE 12 MIN • MAKES 24

1 cup all-purpose flour
$^1/_4$ teaspoon baking soda
$^1/_4$ teaspoon salt
$^1/_2$ cup granulated sugar
4 tablespoons unsalted butter, softened

$^1/_4$ cup + 2 tablespoons thawed frozen pink lemonade concentrate
1 large egg
1 cup confectioners' sugar

1 Preheat the oven to 350°F. Spray 2 large baking sheets with nonstick spray.

2 Combine the flour, baking soda, and salt in a small bowl. With an electric mixer on medium speed, beat the sugar and butter until creamy. Beat in $^1/_4$ cup of the lemonade concentrate and the egg just until blended. Add the flour mixture and beat at low speed just until moistened.

3 Drop the dough by level tablespoons, about 2 inches apart, onto the baking sheets, making a total of 24 cookies. With your fingers, lightly press each mound to make $1^1/_2$-inch rounds. Bake until lightly browned around the edges, 12–15 minutes, rotating the baking sheets halfway through the baking. Let cool on the baking sheets on racks 5 minutes. With a spatula, transfer the cookies to racks and let cool completely.

4 To make the icing, whisk the confectioners' sugar and the remaining 2 tablespoons lemonade concentrate in a small bowl until smooth. Spread a thin layer of icing onto each cookie. Let stand until the icing is set, about 10 minutes.

PER SERVING (1 cookie): 83 Cal, 2 g Fat, 1 g Sat Fat, 0 g Trans Fat, 14 mg Chol, 41 mg Sod, 15 g Carb, 0 g Fib, 1 g Prot, 3 mg Calc. *POINTS* value: **2.**

BACON, TOMATO, AND CHEDDAR FRITTATA, PAGE 12

Dry and Liquid Measurement Equivalents

If you are converting the recipes in this book to metric measurements, use the following chart as a guide.

TEASPOONS	TABLESPOONS	CUPS	FLUID OUNCES
3 teaspoons	1 tablespoon		½ fluid ounce
6 teaspoons	2 tablespoons	1/8 cup	1 fluid ounce
8 teaspoons	2 tablespoons plus 2 teaspoons	1/6 cup	
12 teaspoons	4 tablespoons	¼ cup	2 fluid ounces
15 teaspoons	5 tablespoons	1/3 cup minus 1 teaspoon	
16 teaspoons	5 tablespoons plus 1 teaspoon	1/3 cup	
18 teaspoons	6 tablespoons	¼ cup plus 2 tablespoons	3 fluid ounces
24 teaspoons	8 tablespoons	½ cup	4 fluid ounces
30 teaspoons	10 tablespoons	½ cup plus 2 tablespoons	5 fluid ounces
32 teaspoons	10 tablespoons plus 2 teaspoons	2/3 cup	
36 teaspoons	12 tablespoons	¾ cup	6 fluid ounces
42 teaspoons	14 tablespoons	1 cup minus 2 tablespoons	7 fluid ounces
45 teaspoons	15 tablespoons	1 cup minus 1 tablespoon	
48 teaspoons	16 tablespoons	1 cup	8 fluid ounces

TEASPOONS	
¼ teaspoon	1 milliliter
½ teaspoon	2 milliliters
1 teaspoon	5 milliliters
1 tablespoon	15 milliliters
2 tablespoons	30 milliliters
3 tablespoons	45 milliliters
¼ cup	60 milliliters
1/3 cup	80 milliliters
½ cup	120 milliliters
2/3 cup	160 milliliters
¾ cup	175 milliliters
1 cup	240 milliliters
1 quart	950 milliliters

LENGTH	
1 inch	25 millimeters
1 inch	2.5 centimeters

OVEN TEMPERATURE			
250°F	120°C	400°F	200°C
275°F	140°C	425°F	220°C
300°F	150°C	450°F	230°C
325°F	160°C	475°F	250°C
350°F	180°C	500°F	260°C
375°F	190°C	525°F	270°C

WEIGHT	
1 ounce	30 grams
¼ pound	120 grams
½ pound	240 grams
1 pound	480 grams

Note: Measurement of less than 1/8 teaspoon is considered a dash or a pinch.
Metric volume measurements are approximate.

POWER-KEG CHILI, PAGE 76

INDEX

C

T

CHOCOLATE ANGEL FOOD CAKE WITH ESPRESSO GLAZE, PAGE 191

RECIPES BY POINTS VALUE

RECIPES THAT WORK WITH THE
SIMPLY FILLING TECHNIQUE

AUTUMN POT ROAST WITH HORSERADISH SAUCE, PAGE 118